A Vision o

Queen Mary's Hospital
For Children

Volume II

TRUST QUEEN MARY'S TO CARE FOR YOUR CHILD

A Vision of Healing
Queen Mary's Hospital for Children
Volume II

ISBN: 1 903607 08 6

Typesetting and production by:

Able Publishing
13 Station Road
Knebworth
Herts SG3 6AP

Tel: 01438 812320 / 814316   Fax: 01438 815232
Email: fp@ablepublishing.co.uk
Website: www.ablepublishing.co.uk

Dedication

This book is dedicated to all those who suffer, whether in mind, body or spirit, and to all those who care. May God grant them peace, hope and strength, patience, humility and always purpose.

AND IN EVERLOVING MEMORY OF
MY PARENTS - ROSE AND ERN

*With my parents at the Nutfield 5 mile road race
Easter Monday, 20th April 1987*

To Meler,

With all good wishes
from
Ernest Earl

CONTENTS

H. M. Queen Mary, Patron of the Hospital,
wearing the Insignia of the Garter set in diamonds,
together with the brooch which formed part of the
Coronation gift of the Marys of the Empire.
Photograph taken at Windsor Castle, June 10th 1911

INTRODUCTION

This second volume of my book on Queen Mary's portrays the many human stories that have been sent to me since Book 1 was published. Putting this second book together has been a great joy to both of us. The perfect gems that came through the post, the telephone and in person in response to Book 1 meant that Book 2 'had to be' and we hereby proudly present it.

Some, of course, have memories filled with sadness and others with joy, but they were all treasured. Staff were dedicated to their work and shared in so many of the emotions felt by the children, their parents and loved ones.

The spirit of Queen Mary's will live through these photographs, reminiscences and cameo stories.

Being part of Queen Mary's has been a wonderful privilege and I am proud to present this second volume. It tells of human courage, compassion, devotion to duty, strength of character and purpose, patience, skill, love, hope and the determination to fight on against seemingly overwhelming odds.

Ernest Earl

ACKNOWLEDGEMENTS

I would like to express my full appreciation to all those kind and generous people and organisations that have made this second edition of the Queen Mary's story possible. Acknowledgements accompany the chapter and articles published here.

Numerous people involved with the hospital in a variety of ways, from patients, parents, staff, relatives, friends and volunteers alike have all had a part to play. To list everybody would be a chapter in itself. I thank them all. Some of my helpers have no connection with Queen Mary's, but have generously given their time, skills and energy to assist in the book's production. No organisation or journal editor has asked for copyright fees, which has been a considerable asset to me.

The following list is by no means comprehensive, but it does give some insight into the organisations and people who have made the book possible.

- Queen Mary's Hospital for Children, Child Health Management Committee who gave me permission to write the book.

- My wife Frances who gave me wholehearted, generous and full support throughout its production.

- Mrs Marian Forbes and Mr Richard Hanks, friends and neighbours who painstakingly typed all the material and put it on a computer disk; freely and willingly giving of their time and skills.

- Heather Whitehead for working so hard on classifying material.

- Mr Terry Spurr, Curator, London Ambulance Museum.

- R C N (ARCHIVES) - Staff - Edinburgh.

- Mr Frank Horan - Editor - Journal of Bone & Joint Surgery.

- Mr Peter Baron - Editor - The Northern Echo.

- The Advertiser Series.

- Dr Josephine Hammond - Consultant Paediatrician.

- The Staff of the Durham City Library.

- London Borough of Sutton Library.

- Redhill Library, Surrey.

- Jackie Johnston, Chairman, Redhill Local History Group.

- Robert Wade, Photography Department, St. Helier NHS Hospital and Queen Mary's Hospital for Children.

- Genetta Baird for supplying photographic copies of her oil painting.

- Durham Health Authority and the Staff at Dryburn Hospital for supplying photographs and material on Dryburn Emergency Hospital. (Special thanks to Pathology Department).

- Michelle Minto - Wellcome Trust.

- John Welch - Medical Engineering Resource Unit, Orchard Hill.

- Justin Bradley and Brian Withers for information on miniature railway.

HISTORY OF THE NATIONAL HEALTH SERVICE

The introduction of the National Health Service Act (1946) and its implementation on the 5th July 1948 was the culmination of years of sustained campaigning for an egalitarian system of health care in Britain. The major thrust of the campaign was the setting up of a centrally controlled health care system which divorced 'the ability to get the best health advice and treatment from the ability to pay' (Leathard 1990:30).

The aim of the National Health Service (NHS) was to 'provide a comprehensive and equitable health service' (Allsop and May 1993), 'free at the point of delivery' (Leathard 1990), which would 'secure improvement in the physical and mental health of the people and the prevention, diagnosis and treatment of illness' (Morrison Report 1979:8).

The NHS was funded through taxation. In its first year of operation the actual cost was £433 million. This figure far exceeded expectations and very quickly led to a government reappraisal of one of the major tenets of the NHS, that of 'free at the point of delivery'. In 1951 the then Labour government introduced charges for dentures and spectacles. Charges for dental treatment and prescriptions followed a year later. This fundamental shift in philosophy led to the resignation of three ministers – Bevan, Wilson and Freeman – 'in disgust' (Leathard 1990).

THE STORY OF MY PAINTING

My name is Genetta Mary Baird (née Jackson). I started my RSCN three year training course, at Queen Mary's Hospital for Sick Children in October 1956, and was lucky enough to pass my final exams first time round. I stayed at QMH for the whole of my nursing career.

In early 1960 I was approached by the then Matron, Miss Dilys Jones, and asked if I would sit for Ken Bates, who was the Hospital School art master, in order for him to paint the portrait of "Nurse and Child". To this day I have no idea why I was chosen, maybe it was because my middle name is Mary, but I do feel very privileged to now be part of QMH history!

I can't remember how many sittings it took, but I do remember going to Ken Bates' art studio at his home. He started by making sketches of my head and shoulders, as he explained "to get the feel of my bone structure". He gave me two of those sketches, of which I have one, and my Mother has the other. They are framed and proudly hang in our respective homes. Although I never held the "child" in the painting, only the red blanket, I was told that the child was a patient at that time, and neither did I stand outside in the garden. I think that that was all poetic licence on Ken's part; it does however make for a very attractive background.

The painting, duly finished, was hung in the main entrance hall of the "Admin Block" opposite the picture of Queen Mary herself, an honour indeed. There it hung for many years, quite how many I'm not sure, but I think until Queen Mary's Hospital was moved to St. Helier in November 1993 when, as it turned out, it was put into storage for safe keeping.

My husband (Michael) had always said that if ever the painting was not needed, or put up for sale by the Hospital, he would be very interested in purchasing it. To this end I was given the name of Helena Reeves, who was the public relations and marketing co-ordinator of the St. Helier NHS Trust. I wrote to her on 2nd March 1997, giving as many details as I could, and asking if she had any knowledge of the painting's whereabouts. On 26th March I had a reply saying that Helena had read my letter with interest, and would check to see if the painting was amongst the items in storage. Imagine my surprise and delight to receive a telephone call from Helena one Monday morning in April to say that not only had they found the painting but that they would like to give it to me. I was over the moon! A date was arranged for the presentation by Sir Jeremy Elwes, who was Chairman of their NHS Trust. The time was to be 2.30pm on Friday 20th June 1997 at Queen Mary's, now at St. Helier.

I am now the very proud owner of a unique painting which will be a constant reminder of my many happy days spent at QMH.

PS. In 1989 the "head and shoulders" of the painting was used for a limited edition of 1,000 plates from a design by Neil Fruen, which were produced by Royal Worcester to commemorate *"80 Years of Caring for Children 1909-1989"*.

SANCTVS LVCAS

This stone carving of Saint Luke is situated above the main entrance to the administration building. It depicts Saint Luke the Physician and evangelist with his symbol a winged ox.

ST LUKE – PHYSICIAN AND EVANGELIST

(LUCAS, LOO'KAS, same as Luke)

Saint Luke is the Patron Saint of physicians and surgeons, and also of painters of pictures. He was himself a great artist in words, and his narratives have inspired many masterpieces of art.

Traditional author of the third gospel and the Acts of the Apostles in the New Testament, he was a gentile, a Greek, perhaps born in Antioch, and a medical man by profession. St Paul speaks of him as 'our beloved Luke, the physician'. (Colossians, ko-los-'yans, people of Colosse – iv 14).

Certain passages in the Acts of the Apostles are believed to indicate that the writer was with St Paul on parts of his second and third missionary journeys and on the voyage to Italy when they were shipwrecked off Malta.

St Luke's gospel, addressed to the Gentile world, is remarkable for its tender interest in the sick and outcast, its sympathy with womanhood, its intimate details of the infancy, perhaps derived from the Virgin Mary, and its full treatment of Christ's last journey to

Jerusalem. Its literary charm betokens a versatile and cultivated intellect. Its sequel, the Acts of the Apostles, displays similar qualities. Saint Luke is believed to have died at the age of 84.

SIR GEORGE FREDERIC STILL (1868 – 1941)

Sir George Frederic Still whose portrait is published here by kind permission of THE WELLCOME TRUST MEDICAL PHOTOGRAPHY LIBRARY is referred to by Dr Silva in my first book on Queen Mary's. Sir George Frederic Still was the first paediatrician and was Physician Extraordinary to the King from 1937.

MAJOR JOHN HALL-EDWARDS
– the first x-ray

I am very grateful to Mr David Hoffman for the most interesting information he supplied to me, and the photographs, concerning the discovery of x-rays, and the huge contribution made by his great uncle to the advancement of medical science in this field of medicine at the end of the 19th century. The pioneering work of Major John Hall-Edwards, along with his great courage, cannot be over estimated.

I print his photograph and that of the first x-ray ever taken in my book, not only as a tribute to him, but to give an insight into the problems faced by the medical staff at Queen Mary's in the early days of scientific medical knowledge and discovery. The hospital buildings being constructed during the aforementioned period, and operational in 1909.

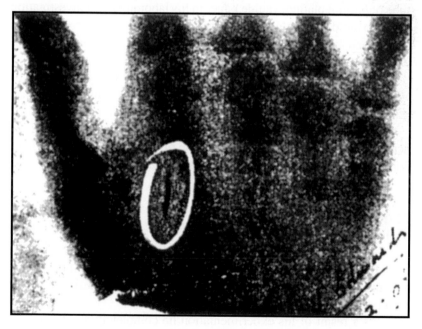

This is the first x-ray taken by Dr Hall-Edwards. The ringed area shows a needle embedded in the hand of a seamstress. It is signed and dated December 1896.

Experiments that he carried out with radiographs in Newhall Street, Birmingham, eventually led to the loss of his left hand and forearm, and four fingers of his right hand.

Following his appointment as Doctor-in-Charge of the x-ray unit at the General Hospital, Birmingham, he became x-ray officer to the Imperial Yeomanry Hospital in the Boer Wars. He insisted that his staff wore protective clothing, but not himself.

He was refused permission to go to France with his x-ray equipment at the outbreak of World War I, and accepted a commission in the Royal Army Medical Corps, treating the wounded at Birmingham's Military Hospitals.

The x-ray 'dermatitis' in his fingers was believed to have been cancer. At the time of his death in 1926, at the age of 68, his x-ray treatment was used throughout England.

The date that x-rays were discovered is believed to be November 8th 1895. Wilhelm Konrad Roentgen observed an unusual line in a tube of barium platinocyanide paper in his laboratory. On investigation he discovered that the luminous effect had come from a Crooke's tube which had been covered with black cardboard. Unable to find an explanation for these invisible rays, he called them x-rays.

The discovery was reported to the Phsyico-Medical Society of Wurzburg and on the 28th December the Society named the newly discovered rays after him.

X-rays are taken for granted in modern society, but applying the science of radiology to patients cost one of its earliest pioneers, Major John Hall-Edwards, initially his hands, and ultimately his life.

Major John Hall-Edwards
18 December 1858 - 15 August 1926

Basically, Roentgen 'discovered' the x-ray, but my great uncle was the first to use it for humanitarian purposes. He qualified at LRCP Edinburgh now University of Birmingham.

As a result of his experimentation he completely lost the use of one arm and almost the other arm as well. As a result of this, and through public outcry, he was awarded a special pension from Parliament authorised by King Edward VII in 1908. In 1914 in spite of having withered hands he was in charge of four functions at the Birmingham Military Hospital.

He was also a fairly proficient painter - only as a hobby - and I do have one of his paintings.

Further he wrote not only many papers but also a very interesting book entitled 'Cancer: Its control and prevention'. This was published in 1926 shortly before his death. He kept back the publication of this book because initially he thought it might spread fear but eventually his great experience persuaded him to do so.

David Hoffman

Major J. F. Hall-Edwards, LRCP, LM(Edin.)

PUGH AND HIS TRACTION

This article was kindly sent to me by former Theatre Sister Margaret Baker and is reproduced by kind permission of Mr Frank Horan, MSc, FRCS, Editor 'Journal of Bone and Joint Surgery' in which this article first appeared. *EE*

The Journal of Bone and Joint Surgery 56B, no. 2, May 1974

William Thomas Gordon Pugh

This article records the contribution made to the care of crippled children by Pugh of Carshalton, the centenary of whose birth fell last year.

William Thomas Gordon Pugh was medical superintendent of Queen Mary's Hospital for Children, Carshalton, from 1909 until his retirement in 1937. Originally a physician, he became interested, of necessity, in children's orthopaedics, and during those twenty-eight years established and directed one of the first long-stay children's country hospitals in the South of England. Both Pugh and his hospital became well known for the management of skeletal tuberculosis and poliomyelitis.

Pugh is best remembered for his "traction by suspension" and for his "Carshalton carriages" which were the tools he used to diminish the destructive changes so manifest in tuberculous joints treated without traction.

William Thomas Pugh was born in 1872 at Hodley, a village in Montgomeryshire. In 1899 he adopted by deed poll the additional Christian name of Gordon. He was educated at Ardwyn School, Aberystwyth, University College, Aberystwyth, and the Middlesex Hospital Medical School, where he was entrance scholar and subsequently Lyell Gold Medallist in practical surgery, Senior Broderip Scholar and Governors' Prizeman. He qualified in 1894 and graduated the following year with first class honours in surgery and honours in medicine and obstetrics After the customary joiner appointments at his teaching hospital and in children's work, he joined the fever service of the Metropolitan Asylums Board in 1897. The following year he gained the M. D. and in 1907 became superintendent of Gore Farm Hospital (now the Southern Hospital) at Dartford in Kent. During 1905 he had described a simple staining technique, using toluidine blue in absolute alcohol and glacial acetic acid, for the detection of the diphtheria bacillus by demonstration of its Babès-Ernst bodies or polar granules (Pugh 1905).

In 1909, as a result of his expressed views on the need for children's country hospitals, he was appointed first Medical Superintendent of the Children's Infirmary at Carshalton, which was, with royal approval, redesigned Queen Mary's Hospital for Children in 1914; here he remained for the rest of his professional career. He retired in 1937 and died at Boscombe, Hampshire, eight years later (D'Arcy power and Le Fanu 1953). By 1919 his reputation was so established in orthopaedics that he became a member of a select orthopaedic club with McRae Aitken, Blundell Bankart, Rowley Bristow, Reginald Elmslie, Laming Evans, William Trethowan, Jenner Verrall and Thomas Fairbank. In 1926 Pugh was president of the Orthopaedic Section of the Royal Society of Medicine. He was an early member of the British Orthopaedic Association, and in 1935 he was elected to the Fellowship of the Royal College of Surgeons of England.

When Pugh arrived at Carshalton, the hospital, which had been completed by the Metropolitan Asylums Board in 1907, consisted in the main of twenty-four single-storey ward blocks with over 900 beds. The buildings were originally intended for a convalescent fever hospital but had never been occupied. They were situated in 136 acres of parkland on the Surrey Downs. Pugh modified some of the ward blocks in order to provide an operating theatre, gymnasium and appliance workshop (Pugh 1926). The reduced bed compliment was made up by constructing verandas around the courtyards on the south side of each ward block in which 300 children might live, day and night, summer and winter, continuously in the open air. Children who required prolonged in-patient treatment were accepted from the whole of the London area on the authority of the boards of guardians and the London County Council.

Under Pugh's guidance special units were set up within the hospital to care for children with skeletal tuberculosis, poliomyelitis, cerebral palsy and rheumatic fever. The undulating countryside provided ideal conditions for the open-air treatment of skeletal tuberculosis so popular at the time. In addition, enforced rest, adequate diet and conservative surgery, which included the aspiration and incision of abscesses, were the mainstays of the treatment. Pugh accepted a trial of heliotherapy (sunshine) and phototherapy (carbon arc lamp), but was not convinced of their efficiency (Pugh 1925-26); however, he was more impressed with the use of radium in the treatment of tuber-culous cervical adenitis (Pugh 1937).

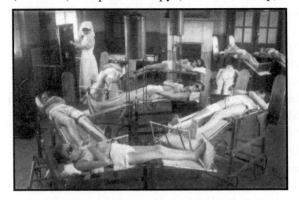

UVR Carbon Arc Lamp 1926/27

Gordon Pugh is best remembered in orthopaedic circles for his methods of overcoming deformity and maintaining enforced rest of the tuberculous hip and spine. In 1924 he introduced into England "traction by suspension" for the treatment of tuberculosis of the hip, at the suggestion of Dennis W. Crile of Chicago (Pugh 1925-26). The method had first been described by Josse of Amiens in 1836 for the treatment of fractures of the femur, and Pott and Petit had experimented with inclined planes and gravity in the eighteenth century (Rang 1966). Pugh had not been satisfied with the ability of weight traction to abolish deformity caused by spasm around an inflamed hip joint.

The original apparatus used at Carshalton consisted of a fracture board and mattress on which the child was placed with the feet towards the head of the bed. Skin extension was applied

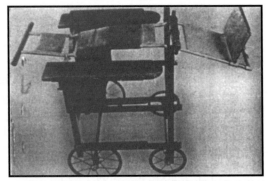

The first spinal carriage

20

Orthopaedic Ward
1925

Teacher in
white coat

to the affected limb. The extension straps were secured to the fracture board and, by attaching it to the head rail, the child was tilted head down at about 30 degrees. Lateral rotation of the limb was prevented by a sandal attached to a horizontal wooden bar, and a further wooden bar was placed under the mattress at knee level to prevent backward subluxation of this joint.

One night of "traction by suspension" usually sufficed to correct hip deformity caused by muscle spasm. The child was allowed relatively free mobility on the bed but was prevented from turning over by a chest band. Pugh had difficulty in finding a suitable skin extension to withstand prolonged traction. Initially, and with success, he used two large moleskin plasters which enveloped the thigh. These were later replaced by two layers of stockinette fixed to the thigh by zinc-gelatin paste which gave fewer skin complications.

Pugh also modified Robert Jones' abduction frame to give traction by suspension in patients with advanced tuberculosis of the hip in whom the desired result was ankylosis in the best position rather than a mobile joint, as was often obtained by "Pugh's traction" in early cases. In the early nineteen-twenties the first tip-up hip carriage was produced and this was essentially the fracture board on wheels, elevated to 30 degrees from the horizontal.

For treatment of spinal caries Pugh advocated prolonged recumbency to prevent the collapse of diseased vertebral bodies until union had been achieved. There were no short cuts; "there had never yet been devised a jacket or splint... which was capable of relieving the diseased vertebral bodies of an erect child from superincumbent weight" (Pugh 1925). He believed that recumbency could prevent

21

deformity in early cases but did not think that hyperextension at the seat of disease, as practised by Gauvain, could produce correction if deformity was already present. Pugh argued that hyperextension opened a gap between the vertebral bodies which interfered with bone healing.

The lesion would then heal with fibrous tissue which allowed recurrence of the deformity on assumption of the upright posture despite the support of a jacket or brace. He was also against posterior spinal bone grafting as a method of shortening the duration of recumbency. He regarded the procedure as performed in the nineteen-twenties and thirties as unsuitable for children. The operation was often done while the disease was still active in an endeavour to reduce weight on the weakened vertebral bodies by bracing the posterior elements together. Pugh argued that the centre of gravity for the body was well in front of the spinal column and that, if recumbency was discontinued before healing was well advanced, collapse of the vertebral bodies could occur anteriorly.

Furthermore, the graft prevented telescoping of the vertebrae and maintained the space between them with a persistent abscess and further sinus formation (Pugh 1925). Pugh was in advance of his time and his views upon spinal grafting—in those days always posterior—proved correct. Pugh attempted to neutralise the deformity after arrest of activity by encouraging the compensatory curvature in the healthy region of the spine. He had observed that in two-thirds of his children spinal caries developed before the age of six years, when the shape of the spine was readily modified (Pugh 1925).

Pugh developed the Carshalton carriages for recumbent treatment

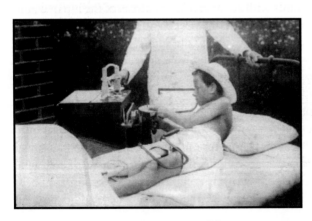

April 1925

of vertebral caries (Pugh 1921). They were made in the hospital workshop and consisted of a metal spinal frame mounted on a wooden carriage. On them, children could be immobilised for months or years with little supervision, but could exercise the limbs and share in the social and educational amenities of the hospital. Constructed of gas piping, the frame was shaped individually for each child to produce the appropriate compensatory spinal curvatures. The child was secured to the frame with a waistcoat of crash towelling and a folding leg piece was incorporated to rest the knees in slight flexion and prevent equinus deformity of the foot. When there was clinical and radiological evidence of healing, many children were then treated for a further lengthy period, often months or years, in a moulded jacket of non-flammable celluloid.

Renal infection and lithiasis were, at one time, common complications in recumbent children and the carriages were modified in the early nineteen-thirties to allow 30 degrees of tilt of the frame to either side, thus elevating each kidney in turn to improve urinary drainage. This, in addition to a high fluid intake, restriction of dietary oxalate and oral administration of potassium citrate, solved the problem.

In 1933 Pugh introduced a second hip carriage in which the spinal frame was mounted on rollers on a backward inclined slope to produce traction by suspension. As on the spinal carriage, a rotary device was incorporated. This carriage was developed to allow a child to lie in a more comfortable horizontal position.

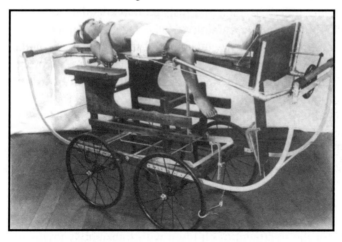

The hip carriage, which could tilt sideways

Foot Corrective Exercises 1926

Elmslie had reported that poliomyelitis was the commonest single cause of crippling in children in the London area (Pugh 1922-23) and, in 1924, the London County Council designated fifty beds at Queen Mary's Hospital for the treatment of this condition in the second stage, that is, from the loss of muscle tenderness until the disease became stationary. Pugh did not believe in out-patient treatment, as was commonly practised then, and insisted that adequate supervision with rest, splintage, muscle training and re-education could only be done in hospital. In some cases he considered that heat, massage, and electrical stimulation were beneficial, although he was fully aware of the dangers of fatigue. All treatment was under the supervision of two gymnasts. An outdoor heated swimming pool was constructed for the use of these patients in 1927. Children in the later stages of the disease were also admitted for operative correction of their deformities and for stabilisation procedures, and many of these were done by distinguished visiting orthopaedic surgeons such as the redoubtable Willie Trethowan from Guy's.

Although skeletal tuberculosis is now uncommon in the United Kingdom, Pugh's "traction by supervision" remains of considerable value for the treatment of children with transient synovitis of the hip, Legg-Calvé-Perthes' disease, coxa vara (Watson-Jones 1952) and fractures of the femoral shaft, and provide a memento of "Pugh of Carshalton" who devoted his life to the care of crippled children.

I am grateful to Mr Geoffrey Walker for his continued encouragement and advice in the preparation of this article. I also thank all those who provided historical and other details of Pugh, especially his son, Surgeon Captain P. D. G. Pugh O.B.E., R.N., and Mr V. S. Patel, who carried out some of the research. Miss M. Pugh (unrelated to W. T. G. Pugh's family) prepared all the illustrations from the contemporary originals. Financial assistance was provided by the South West Metropolitan Regional Hospital Board.

Medical Superintendent's House 1950

A much abridged version of this paper was presented to the Orthopaedic section of the Royal Society of Medicine on June 12, 1971.

B. D. A. Morris, M. B., B. S. (Lond.), F. R. C. S. (Eng)
London England

METROPOLITAN ASYLUMS BOARD

Queen Mary's Hospital For Children, Charshalton, Surrey

INSPECTION, SATURDAY 2ND JULY, 1927

PROGRAMME OF ARRANGEMENTS

Trains leave Victoria (Southern railway - Brighton Section) at 1.48 and 1.50 p.m., and London Bridge at 1.53 p.m. for *Sutton*. These trains will be met; members and visitors will be conveyed from Sutton station to the hospital in the Board's motor omnibuses. (Electric trains also leave Victoria at 2.10 p.m., and at intervals of 20 Minutes for *Carshalton Beeches*, which is 12 minutes walk from the hospital).

2.40 p.m.   Arrival at the hospital. Parties will be conducted over the hospital and the work of its various departments explained.

4.30 p.m.   Tea.

4.30 to 6 p.m.   Children's fête.

Return trains leave *Sutton* for Victoria at 4.50, 5.10, 5.30 and 6.00 p.m.; for London Bridge at 4.40, 5.35 and 6.24 p.m. Electric trains leave *Carshalton Beeches* for Victoria at 4.32 p.m. and at intervals of 20 minutes up to 6 p.m. and of 30 minutes subsequently.

Metropolitan Asylums Board Ambulance 1880

and circa 1918

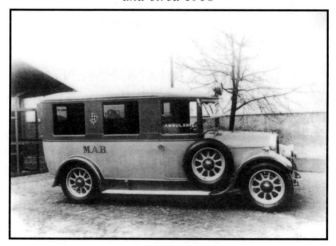

The photographs of the horse drawn ambulance and early motorised ambulance are printed here by kind permission of:

Mr Terry Spurr, Curator, London Ambulance Service,
NHS Trust Museum, Ilford, Essex

The ambulances appeared on the Channel 4 programme 'Collectors' Lot'. I am grateful to their staff for putting me in touch with Mr Spurr. *EE*

QUEEN MARY'S HOSPITAL FOR CHILDREN

Queen Mary's Hospital for Children is situated at Carshalton on the Surrey Downs in a park of 136 acres. The site was purchased in 1896 for £13,550, and the capital outlay to Michaelmas, 1914, amounted to £309,788. The buildings were originally designed as a convalescent fever hospital, but unforeseen circumstances having freed one of the River hospitals for this purpose, the institution became available for other uses. Thus it came about that, when the Local government board proposed, as a means of relieving the pressure on the accommodation for sick poor in the metropolis, that the Metropolitan Asylums Board should undertake the care of such sick children as were suitable for removal from the infirmaries, their request could at once be complied with. The board had already realised the advantage of treating sick London children in a country hospital, a principle which is now generally recognised, and on 26 January, 1909, the hospital at Charshalton, in healthy and bracing surroundings, was opened by the Board with Dr. W. T. Gordon Pugh as medical superintendent.

GENERAL ARRANGEMENTS

The institution was designed by Messrs. Treadwell & Martin, and built by Messrs. W. Johnson & Co., Ltd. It drained into the public sewers of the Urban District Council of Charshalton; electricity supplied by the South Metropolitan Electric Tramways and Lighting Company; gas by Croydon Gas company and water by the Sutton Water company; rainwater reservoir with a capacity of 175,00 gallons is also provided under the drying ground. The whole institution is heated, and hot water is supplied, from the central boiler-house.

In close proximity to the latter are the workshops, laundry, disinfector, destructor, coal store and transformer house. The stores and the central kitchen, equipped with labour-saving appliances, are near to the administrative block. Meals are delivered to the wards, and the other internal transport work is effected by motor vehicles. The staff are conveyed to and from the station by a motor-bus, and garages are provided for the cars. An electric time circuit ensures uniform time throughout the hospital.

THE ACCOMMODATION FOR PATIENTS AND STAFF

The hospital contains 900 beds, the accommodation being provided in sixteen ward blocks and in two isolation blocks. In addition to the administrative block and two large staff homes, there are six small staff homes, one attached to each of the six 'streets' of blocks, and each containing the quarters of the superintendent sister in charge of the 'street' and twelve bedrooms for nursing staff. The ward sisters also have sitting and bedroom accommodation in these staff homes. The administrative block is placed in a central position, a main central avenue running north and south, connecting both it and the kitchen and stores block in the rear of it with the two isolation blocks which lie at the extreme southern part of the hospital.

From this central avenue six 'streets' arranged *en echelon*, give access to the ward blocks and staff homes appertaining to them. Distributed among these blocks are the departments for electro-therapeutics, for radiography, and for dental and eye diseases, the gymnasium, the operation theatre, the laboratory, and the surgical appliance workshops. The recreation hall equipped with a cinematograph and with school-rooms attached. A chapel and a mortuary are also provided.

In the hospital workshops practically all the appliances in use are constructed, and discharged patients are invited to attend when their appliances need repair or re-adjustment.

TREATMENT BY LIGHT AND FRESH AIR

In 1912, verandas, each containing thirty beds, were added to ten of the ward blocks, thus enabling 300 children to lie in the open air, winter and summer, day and night, almost completely free from colds and from infectious diseases. Competition for these veranda beds is very keen in the summer moths, and even in the winter the children get accustomed to the open air and thoroughly enjoy it. Extensive use is made of direct sunlight, and the courtyards, open only to the south, with verandas on the three remaining sides, are ideal for carrying out this treatment. The orthopaedic carriages designed by the medical superintendent have proved of great value, particularly in carrying out sunlight treatment, for they enable the patients who are accommodated indoors to reap to the full during the day the benefits derived from light, air and sunshine. For the treatment of lupus, and for general use during the months when effective treatment by direct sunlight is not possible in this country, a light department was established some years ago.

SCOPE OF THE HOSPITAL WORK

The hospital is a general hospital for children, the patients varying in age from a few weeks to sixteen years, and suffering from a variety of diseases. It undertakes the surgery of a number of the Board's institutions for children, including the training ship Exmouth with its 700 boys. The unusual facility for open-air treatment has led to a large number of beds being devoted to children suffering from non-pulmonary tuberculosis. Orthopaedic surgery figures largely in the work of the hospital, which possesses the great advantage over most voluntary and private institutions of being able to keep in-patients almost indefinitely, taking in a large number of cases given up elsewhere. At the present time, about one third of the patients admitted are orthopaedic cases, one-third have surgical tuberculosis, and one-third suffer from various other diseases.

During the last year developments have occurred particularly in connection with the treatment of two of the more serious diseases of childhood, namely, rheumatism and poliomyelitis in the earlier stages.

THE RHEUMATIC UNIT

Since September, 1926, a unit of 60 beds has been reserved for children suffering from rheumatic fever, acute endocarditis or chorea. These beds are utilised for research, particularly of a bacteriological nature, and Dr. Lazarus Barlow, one of the Board's bacteriologists, devotes his whole time to the investigation of the disease, the hospital being equipped with a research laboratory and animal house.

POLIOMYELITIS

For many years the Board has provided accommodation for poliomyelitis at their infectious hospitals during the first or acute stage, which lasts two or three months and at Queen Mary's Hospital during the third stage, that of operative correction. The attention of the Board was called, however, to the fact that, although the voluntary hospitals also admitted to their wards patients in these two stages in considerable numbers, there was an inadequate provision for treatment during the second or convalescent stage, which extends for a period varying from one to two years from the end of the acute stage. As they were informed that in many cases an unnecessary degree of deformity resulted from this fact, it was decided to reserve a block of 40 beds for this stage at Queen Mary's hospital, and to equip it specially for this purpose. Recently the construction of an out-of-door pool has been authorised for underwater gymnastic exercises in connection with muscle re-education, which forms an important part of the treatment.

EDUCATION OF PATIENTS

While the average stay is one year, a large proportion of the patients remain under treatment for four years or more. As many of these children have spent much of their lives previously in hospital it is obvious that they would be quite illiterate if they were not taught while under treatment at Queen Mary's Hospital. Indeed, the need for education was shown by a report made in 1920, from which it appeared that of 192 children with learning difficulties over 11 years of age who where admitted, the retardation in 79 cases was three years, in 54 four years, and in 59 five or more years; some in the last group, however, were probably mentally defective. There is a full-time staff of 25 teachers, the expenditure on education during the year ended 31st March, 1927, being £5,821. Teaching is carried out in 20 wards, where the great majority of the children are in bed, many classes being held in the open courtyard, and in the hall, where the convalescent children attend. the curriculum is kept as wide as possible, and includes many varieties of handwork. Every child's progress in reading, writing and arithmetic is tested and reported on twice a year, and a record is kept for the whole period of its stay, being passed on from ward to ward as the child is transferred. These records show a good average progress during the year, especially when the limited school hours are taken into consideration, children with problems due to a lack of opportunity making good progress.

THE TRAINING OF PROBATIONER NURSES

A well equipped lecture and demonstration room is provided and two whole-time sister-tutors are engaged in instructing the probationer nurses. A probationer during the first year attends lectures on anatomy, physiology, hygiene and general nursing. During the second and third years she attends elementary lectures on medicine and surgery conducted by the medical staff in addition to demonstrations by sister-tutors. she is required on the completion of three years' training to enter for the State examination in the Nursing of Sick Children as arranged by the General Nursing Council for England and Wales, this hospital being recognised by the Council as one in which their prescribed training is carried out. If she passes this examination her name is placed on the appropriate State Register as a sick children's nurse.

THE METROPOLITAN ASYLUMS BOARD

Chairman : Mr Francis Morris, J.P.
Vice-Chairman : The Rt. Hon. The Viscount Doneraile

CHILDREN'S COMMITTEE
Chairman : Rev. Canon Hubert Curtis, M.A.
Vice-Chairman : Sir Robert Walden, C.B.E., D.L., J.P

QUEEN MARY'S HOSPITAL SUB-COMMITTEE
Chairman : Miss M. E. Broadbent

Miss H. M. M. Cunningham	Mr. H. S. Mount Somerby
Mr William Evans	Mr. James Sawyer
Mr. N. W. Hubbard, J.P.	Miss Ruth Whitbread

The Chairman and the Vice-Chairman of the Board and the Chairman and the Vice-Chairman of the Children's Committee *ex-officio*.

Medical Superintendent: W. T. Gordon Pugh, M. D., B. S. (Lond.).

Matron: Miss M. Winmill

Steward: Mr. J. R. Earnshaw

Clerk to the Board: Sir Allan Powell, C.B.E.

OFFICE OF THE BOARD, VICTORIA EMBANKMENT, LONDON, E.C.4.

METROPOLITAN ASYLUMS BOARD
YEAR - BOOK 1928-1929

Queen Mary's Hospital for Children
Charshalton, Surrey
(*until March, 1911, known as The Children's Infirmary*)
Stations: Carshalton and Carshalton Beeches.
Telephone, Wallington 2321-2

(*For sick children*)
This institution (which was built and intended for use as a convalescent fever hospital) was opened on 29th January, 1909. The site consists of 136.5 acres, and was purchased in July, 1897, for £13,650. The rateable value is £8,500.

A portion of the site (about 42.5 acres) has been let on lease for seven years, from 25th March, 1924, at an annual rental of £100. - *Board Minutes*, 17th November, 1923, p.200.

Sixty beds are provided for the treatment of rheumatic infection in childhood.

The Board have decided to provide 350 additional beds at this hospital for London children suffering from rheumatic infections. The plans have been approved and it is anticipated that a tender for the works which are estimated to cost about £200,000 will be accepted during the summer of 1928.

The visiting day for adult relatives of children is: Sunday, from 2.00 p.m. to 4.00 p.m.

This hospital has been approved by the General Nursing Council as a training school for sick children's nurses.

SUB COMMITTEE

CUNNINGHAM, Miss H. M. M., HUBBARD, N. W.,
MOUNT SOMERBY, H.S., CURTIS, Rev. Canon HUBERT,
SAWYER, JAMES, WHITBREAD, Miss RUTH, EVANS, WILLIAM

And one rota member each month.
Chairman - Rev. Canon HUBERT CURTIS, M.A. (since June, 1928).

PRINCIPAL OFFICERS

Name, Office, and date of appointment, Annual remuneration.

Pugh, W.T. Gordon, M.D., B.S..
Medical superintendent. Dec., 1908 (Entered the service Nov., 1897)
+ £1,350; unfurnished house.

Trethowan, W. H., F.R.C.S., M.B., B.S.
*Orthapaedic surgeon. Oct., 1919
200 guineas; meals when on duty.

Earnshaw, J. R.
Steward. April, 1921. (Entered the Service Sept., 1899).
£600

Cole, Miss M. A.
Matron. Oct., 1927.
£350; board, lodging, and washing.

Whittington, T. H., M.D., B.S.
*Oculist. June, 1914.
£100.

Corbould, Rev. W.R.
*Chaplain. April, 1920.
Dentist £200

*Annual appointment.
+ Also receives £200 as chief medical officer, children's institutions and surgical tuberculosis service.

LONDON COUNTY COUNCIL

HANDBOOK of General and Special Hospitals and Ancillary Services 1936

QUEEN MARY'S HOSPITAL FOR CHILDREN
Carshalton, Surrey
Telephone: Wallington 2321
Date of opening: 29th January, 1909

History: The area is about 136.5 acres and was purchased by the Metropolitan Asylums Board in July, 1897. A portion of the site (about 42.5 acres) was let on lease from 25th March, 1924 until recently. On this land it is proposed to build a new establishment for the manufacture of antitoxin etc. The hospital was originally built and intended for use as a convalescent fever hospital.

Visiting days for adult relatives: Sundays, bank holidays, Good Friday and Christmas Day, from 2.00 p.m. to 4.00 p.m.

Accommodation: Patients: 1,285 (including 56 isolation beds); sick staff, 48.

Consultants' group No VII

Pathology: Served by Southern group laboratory. Routine pathology performed in hospital laboratory.

Hospital Committee: Mr. G.P. Blizard, J.P. (Chairman); Mrs. G.E. Grenn (Vice-Chairman); Miss M.E. Broadbent; Mrs. Frances Rodd; Mrs. E. Speakman; Mrs. Elsie Sullivan.

Times of meetings: Four-weekly on Wednesdays at 11.15 a.m.

STAFF
Medical superintendent; W.T. Gordon Pugh, M.D., B.S., F.R.C.S.
Matron: Miss M.A. Cole, S.R.N.
Steward: J.R. Earnshaw

MEDICAL AND NURSING EDUCATION

Medical

Demonstrations are given to students from the medical schools by arrangement.

Nursing

The hospital is a recognised training school for registration by the General Nursing Council of England and Wales on the register of sick children's nurses. The training is for three years. Well equipped lecture and demonstration rooms are provided, and there is a qualified sister tutor on the staff.

MAJOR WORKS (completed since 1st April, 1930).
Two single-storey ward blocks, with verandas, four nurses' homes with staff kitchen, serveries and messrooms, and a chapel.

London County Council

HANDBOOK of General and Special Hospitals
and Ancillary Services 1936

SUMMARY OF PATIENTS' ACCOMMODATION
PROVIDED IN SPECIAL HOSPITALS

Hospital	In special wards	In ordinary wards	Total
HOSPITALS FOR INFECTIOUS DISEASES-			
Brook	104	448	552
Eastern	151	470	621
Grove	184	432	616
Northern (part)	60	278	338
North-Eastern (under reconstruction)	46	328	374
North-Western	75	335	410
Park	172	480	652
Southern-			
Upper	118	639	757
Lower	36	731	767
South-Eastern	96	384	480
South-Western	129	234	363
Western	158	363	521
River hospitals-			
Joyce Grenn	150	836	986
Long Reach	-	248	248
Orchard	-	664	664
Smallpox receiving station	-	24	24
OTHER HOSPITALS-			
Post-encephalitis lethargica, Northern (part)	16	282	298
Venereal disease, Sheffield street	4	98	102*
Totals	**1,499**	**7,274**	**8,773**

* 20 cots included

TUBERCULOSIS HOSPITALS:-

Colindale hospital	349
St. George's home	50
Grove Park hospital	322
Heatherwood hospital	244
High Wood hospital for children (part)	272
King George V sanatorium	232
Millfield convalescent hospital	98
Northern hospital (part)	100
Pinewood sanatorium	160
Princess Mary's hospital for children	Closed
St. Luke's hospital, Lowestoft	210
Queen Mary's hospital for children (part)	260
	2,297

CHILDREN'S HOSPITALS:-

General

Queen Mary's hospital for children (part)	634
The Downs hospital for children (part)	180

Ophthalmia

White Oak hospital	364

Ringworm and other contagious skin diseases

Goldie Leigh hospital (part)	198

*Convalescent**

St. Anne's home	127
Goldie Leigh hospital (part)	50

Rheumatism

High Wood hospital for children (part)	210
Queen Mary's hospital for children (part)	390
The Downs hospital for children (part)	180
	2,333

Grand total	**13,403 beds**

Convalescent children are also accommodated at the Southern hospital and Millfield hospital.

PATIENTS' ACCOMMODATION

Classification	No. of wards	No. of beds	Other special features
Ordinary	37*	1228*	There are departments for massage, physio-therapeutics, radiography, and clinical photography, and for dental and eye diseases.
Isolation wards	5	56	
Special units:-			There are also a gymnasium, operating theatre, laboratory and a workshop for making of surgical appliances.
Surgical tuberculosis	-	260	
Rheumatism	-	390	
Orthopaedic cases	There are no prescribed numbers of beds for these special units, but are included in the figures above.		A chapel and a recreation hall, equipped and a cinematograph, are provided.
Congenital malformation			
Poliomyelitis			There is a fully organised school with a head teacher, assistant head teacher and a staff of 35 assistant teachers.
Uro-genital affections.			

* Including special units.

PATIENTS' STORIES

FRIENDS

It is my joy in life to find
  At every turning of the road
The strong arm of a comrade kind
  To help me onward with my load.
And since I have no gold to give,
  And love alone must make amends,
My only prayer is, while I live:
  God make me worthy of my friends!

Frank Dempster Sherman

"When love is greatest, words are fewest"

American Proverb

"Nature, time and patience are the three great physicians."

H. G. Bonn

Evelyn Ellis - Patient March 1918 to February 1919

Evelyn with fellow patients outside Ward D7/8 1918

Evelyn Ellis was taken by ambulance from the Fulham Road Infirmary (now St. Stephen's Hospital) to Queen Mary's Hospital for Children in March 1918, suffering from anaemia. The doctor felt that she needed country air in order to aid her recovery.

On her arrival at Queen Mary's, Evelyn was taken to Ward Block D7/8 and stayed there for 11 months, describing her stay as a very happy one. Evelyn was on an all girls ward and there was no mixing with children on other wards. (Mixed wards came in 1959 with Dr. Lawson). Her treatment was free.

Church services were held in a church at the top of the hospital. and Evelyn was confirmed there. Near D7/8 was a schoolhouse, with a headmistress and two classrooms; Evelyn attended this school.

In February 1919 Evelyn was considered well enough to leave the hospital and was discharged by Dr Pugh, the first superintendent doctor at Queen Mary's.

Evelyn returned to her home near Parsons Green in Fulham and soon after met one of her nurses in Wandsworth

Evelyn on her discharge from Queen Mary's February 1919

Bridge. The nurse invited Evelyn to her home and took her out every weekend in her car. On another occasion Evelyn went on holiday to Folkstone and met her Queen Mary's teacher who then corresponded with her.

I met Evelyn at the home of her niece and nephew situated near the original Queen Mary's site. It was a privilege to meet Evelyn and her family and I am very pleased to be able to recount her memories.

Evelyn with her nephew Paul and my wife Frances at the new Queen Mary's, 21st May 1997

Evelyn with her friend May who was an Aunt to the Fountain children for 20 years, 7th July 1996

Letter from Mr Francis Compton

I was born on the 2nd November 1927 and am now 72 years old.

When I was two years old, my mother was bathing me one evening when she noticed a small lump on my spine. The doctor sent me to the Queen Elizabeth Hospital in Hackney where it was found I had TB of the spine.

When I was three, I was transferred to Queen Mary's Hospital, Carshalton. The Queen Elizabeth has now closed.

Some points I remember about Carshalton are being on a spinal carriage for four to six years.

Some days, myself and one or two others would manage to release the brakes on the carriages with our big toes and have races around the grounds. I don't remember the names of many staff except Dr Pugh and Sister Benan.

I was in Carshalton Hospital until I was 12½ years old and then transferred to a Hastings & Sevenoaks Society home.

I remember a lady called Mrs Biggs from TOC H who visited me now and again. She was very kind. (My mum and dad were very poor.) Superintendent was a Mr Blake.

Philip Evans - Patient 1932 - 1941

MY MEMORIES

The Harry Gold Band and the fair in the hospital grounds; being bombed out and some of the boys throwing roof slates; nurses pushing me out on to the veranda when I was well enough during the summer months …

On the day that I left Queen Mary's there was a big party for me. However, when my parents came to fetch me, I cried all the way to my sister's in Brixton, as I wanted to go back to the hospital. It was very strange to see buses and trams and I was frightened by them.

I was very near to death on three occasions but my mother said that I would soon be playing football with my friends.

When I was 16 years of age my hip scar re-opened and I went to Dulwich Hospital for treatment. In 1948 I was called up for National Service and, after being demobbed, spent three years in the Territorial Army.

Phil is pictured here in the middle of the photograph with his sister Pat and her husband, Alan.

John Fennell's Report 1933/1934

9/4/97

In the spring of 1933 at the age of 7 I was taken ill and after treatment at home by our G. P. I was diagnosed as having pneumonia and on May 15th I entered the children's ward of Dulwich Hospital. At this time we were living in Peckham. I do not remember what treatment I received - probably only poultices, medicine and TLC in the pre antibiotic era. I do recall being x-rayed about four times and having a number of sessions of sunlamp treatment. I gradually improved and was taken off the danger list. Not understanding this, I was a little disappointed because I could no longer be visited at any time or on any day, but only at weekends.

By September 1933 I was well enough to be transferred to Queen Mary's Hospital at Carshalton. There were a number of immediate

John aged 7/8 years,
Clipstone, Mansfield

changes, of which the one I recall most clearly was the dayroom, a communal area were there were books, games and toys, some of our own, others being part of the hospital equipment.

We were on the ground floor and could see grass and trees whereas at Dulwich the ward must have been on the first or second floor with only a view over rooftops, and being confined to bed most of the time didn't help very much. QMH was much more to children's scale, though I suppose the rooms were of similar proportion to domestic houses, and so seemed less forbidding after the long wards and high ceilings at Dulwich.

Much of the contrast was, of course, due to the change from being a sick child to a convalescent one - we had our meals at a table in the dayroom instead of on trays over the bed, and it was generally of a higher standard and served hot! Very few of the meals stay in my memory except for mugs of cocoa mentioned by another contributor, and apparently unlimited supplies of bread, butter and jam at tea-time. I remember that some slices of bread and butter tasted differently to others, which years later I realised must have been slightly rancid butter in a pre-fridge era. There was a frequency of bread and butter pudding at lunch, with rice, semolina or tapioca as variations and steamed pudding with custard as weekly treats. Getting up for meals had what I now think of as a morale booster for I thought that if I was up and dressed for meals I must be getting better, rather than the other way around!

We had lessons in the dayroom, but they did not seem to occupy much of the day, possibly an hour or two in the mornings. Some of this time was taken up with reading, which I had always enjoyed. We were encouraged to run about outside with a football, but in an informal, unstructured way and it never mattered how many goals were scored and by whom.

One of my strongest recollections is of sleeping out under the veranda which I thought was a great adventure. We had piled up blankets and of course the glass roof. I remember waking up during the night to see the bare tree trunks and branches gleaming ghostly white with hoar frost, which must have been late in October or November. From this I think I must have been in C block as I don't remember any buildings in front of our veranda. November 5th was a memorable occasion because of the fireworks display organised by the staff. I had a good view as I was still sleeping outside at the time and can still visualise the Catherine wheels spinning on the trees and sometimes falling off to chase the Doctor in charge! At Christmas there was a Tableaux from Peter Pan in a corner of the dayroom, complete with Captain Hook, a treasure chest and a realistic crocodile - stuffed or modelled in papier mache. There was no performance of Peter Pan but the story was read to us by the nurses.

One point on which i differ from your 1930 contributor - we had proper toilet-paper rolls and not bundles of railway handbills - so this may have been due to three years of progress! Also I think I wore my own clothes and pyjamas. I clearly remember the day I left QMH - on 8th January, 1934 - when I was taken to reception and asked if there was anyone I knew - and there was my father! It was also the first time I can remember going on a train, though it may not have been my first such journey.

A lot had happened in the eight months I had been away - half of that time at Queen Mary's. I had left from a flat in Peckham and came home to a house in Catford: I joined a new school and made new friends, one of whom became my "best man" 21 years later; My six month old baby sister had become a recognisable person of over a year old, and I had had a birthday at Queen Mary's. My eight months away did not leave any permanent damage as far as I know, and although I was a little short winded and was never able to excel at athletics I held my own at rugby and hockey.

I recovered from my illness at Dulwich, but I am sure that Queen Mary's gave me enormous help in regaining full health, and for that I am very thankful.

Vera Dean

Vera was born in January 1929. At the age of 2½ years she was admitted to Ward F7/8, and stayed until she was five years old. Following her discharge from Queen Mary's, Vera stayed at home until she was twelve years old, having been considered 'too handicapped for school'.

Home was behind Brixton prison. By the time that Vera reached eleven years of age the Second World War had broken out. Her father died in 1940 and her brother Stan was killed in war service while serving in the RAF.

At the age of twelve years Vera went back to Queen Mary's with a ward full of girls who had rheumatism. During the bombing of the hospital in 1940 the ward was evacuated to Cuckfield in Sussex for a year.

Vera with Nurse Diane Noot at the Cerebral Palsy Unit 1932

Vera said that the medical staff were puzzled over her diagnosis. Believing her to be mentally disabled she was transferred to the Cerebral Palsy Unit.

In 1943 Eirene Collis, a Pioneering Physiotherapist, came into the ward with the medical superintendent Dr Evans. He said to Eirene "If you can treat Vera, you can have a job here." Vera being the first patient to be admitted to the Cerebral Palsy Unit.

Eirene Collis, whose work is mentioned in my first book on Queen Mary's, was born in Ireland. She was married to a writer and had two children, Elizabeth and Gabriel. The family moved abroad to Baltimore, where Eirene was trained in the treatment of people suffering from Cerebral Palsy, by Dr Phelps. Returning to England, she practised her new acquired skills at Queen Mary's.

At the age of 16 years Vera had started to walk and read. Although she had little schooling, Vera 'picked up' the ability to read from her sister's teaching.

Vera remained at the hospital until she was twenty years of age and assisted in the care of the other children on the ward. After leaving Queen Mary's Vera went to St Benedict's Hospital in Tooting, South London.

In 1944 Queen Mary's was completely evacuated and Vera went to a hospital in Brentwood, Essex, that specialised in helping people suffering from epilepsy. Vera was away from Queen Mary's for about four months and was discharged in 1948.

I met Vera for the first time on the l0th May 1999 having been introduced by Mrs Sylvia Stronge, former Queen Mary's Hospital School Teacher who is now working with her.

Vera recounted her very moving story to me and also gave me a copy of her own book 'Three Steps Forward.'

"A remarkable and brave woman." Ernest Earl

A Little Girl from Belfast - Dorothy Anderson

I suppose I was a very scared little girl. A new world confronted me. Some of the staff wore white coats, and had strange accents. Having treatment sessions to attend, and being laid flat on a table for that treatment, and worst of all being parted from Mummy. Daddy had come over with us, and came back and forwards at intervals, but he still had his job in Belfast. My late parents would have done anything to help their little girl! For a child of five and a half, these were daunting experiences. Was it any wonder I screamed. I had been sent to Queen Mary's from Northern Ireland to the Cerebral Palsy Unit run by the late Mrs. Collis. Oh yes, Mummy stayed in England to look after me, but she wasn't with me all the time as she previously had been. However, I was only a Day Patient, and Mummy collected me in the afternoon to take me back to our lodgings, i.e. except for the time I had my tonsils removed, and was admitted to another Ward, and nearly screamed the place down when Mummy came to visit me - when she wasn't there it seems I was as good as gold. But at that stage I was older and had settled, when in the C. P. Unit.

"One more chance," my Mother was told. We were referred to

see Dr. Dunham, a friend of Mrs. Collis and consultant on Cerebral Palsy to the London County Council. For some reason, I'm not sure why, but after that appointment, I began to settle down. I was at Q. M. for three and a half years. I attended hospital school at Q. M., my first teacher being the late Miss Audrey Hill, who was followed by the late Mary Tweddle nee Densham. Miss Muriel Taylor was also there. I was put off my feet completely for a time, and teachers and parents had to carry me over their shoulders like sacks of coal. It was crucial furniture be the right height and correct posture was of paramount importance. I was banned from handling any thing fine, and even cutlery had to be fitted with thick wooden handles. The late Mr. Grant did a lot of this work. He was a kindly man.

I also had to walk, or try to walk on skis joined together by two metal bars. These were blocks of wood to which our feet (in boots) were strapped. The toe of the ski was built up containing a hole in the middle of each ski, in which a pole was fitted, but I was useless at using the poles and they had to take them off me. I also had to walk on a highly polished floor with my hands in two pockets of the apron I was wearing.

Dorothy finger painting - Cerebral Palsy Unit 1950s

The mothers were allowed to attend lectures run by Mrs. Collis. In this way Mummy learnt a lot about Cerebral Palsy, and so she was able to carry on with my routine treatment long after we left Q. M. I was diagnosed with 'Tension Athetoid Quadraplegia'. (This is only one type of C. P. of which there are about five or six). Mummy often got fed up being asked by people "what was wrong with me"? On one occasion, when back in Belfast, she was asked this by an acquaintance. When she used the above term, (which was of course correct) the lady never asked her again!

Cerebral Palsy, as the name suggests, has to do with the brain. In my own case it was apparently a Birth Injury. I well remember seeing the brain Mrs Collis kept in a glass case, I think, outside her office - it was very interesting! Mrs Collis, a Physiotherapist from Dublin, had studied Cerebral Palsy in depth, and had devised a way to treat it. She believed that the younger she got a child the better, before that child started forming bad habits in posture and so on.

I made some life long friends through Queen Mary's, amongst Staff and Patients, and still keep in touch with some of them. About two or three years ago, when visiting Miss Taylor, she took me on a nostalgic tour of Queen Mary's grounds. She also took me to visit Sister Hayman, and the late Mrs. Bertha Nicholson. It was lovely to see them again, plus the lay-out of the wards and so on, with the wide expanses of green. I have never forgotten my time at Queen Mary's even though I was so young.

Joan Ross

Here I am on my own with my little cat Susie. Independent of my nearest relatives, which is how it should be. My sister Margaret, and her family, who live 11 miles away. Margaret is my best friend, there for me if I need her, as I am for her and her family. I work part time. My home is very comfortable and warm. It was my parents' home. Over the past four years I have had it adapted to suit my needs and decorated it to my taste. I lost my mother four years ago; my father died last year but had lived in a nursing home for three and a half years. I have carers coming in to cook me a hot meal of my choice, and cook under my instructions every day; and to make my breakfast three days a week when I work. They also tidy up, see to Susie's food, and do my bulky shopping. I pay someone to clean the flat once a week. I am waiting to be assessed by Haringey Social Services with regard to paying for my care which is very worrying because the extra costs of disability are already very high.

I have cerebral palsy, athetoid, and have lately developed arthritis in my spine. It was a terrible blow to discover the onset of arthritis because I learnt to walk in my teens and became very active as far as getting out and about using public transport for many years. Now, I rely on my car and electric scooter to get out and about; because I am less mobile.

I am very grateful to my parents for the tools they gave me to use to cope with daily life. I was an only child until the age of 12 years. I do not think that I was spoilt, but my mother in particular was a very strong willed person, and fought for me to be educated at a local school (education was not compulsory), which was eventually agreed on on the condition that my mother attended to my toilet needs, fed me, etc. throughout the school day. My mother gave me my Christian faith which has grown with me throughout the years, a great comfort in bad times. There are many occasions to praise God for answering prayers; and letting me know so often that He is there for me. Going to a local school and belonging to a local church has given me a great sense of belonging to my local community. My third essential tool for living with a disability is my sense of humour which I definitely inherited from my mother. I have gathered a couple more tools for myself. Mixing with able children at a very early age taught me to explain my disabilities quite openly. I could explain it away in one sentence, "I cannot walk but I can crawl". I had a very happy childhood.

I was twelve years old when I overheard my grandmother say to a friend that it was a pity I did not die at birth. It was the first time I realised the significance of my disability. It was to be the first of many unkind remarks that I would encounter in my adult life, many of which I have forgotten. However my grandmother's remark will always stay with me. I believe that it has had a very positive influence on my life. Realising that I did nearly lose my life at birth I began to question why I was here and what is my purpose in this world? The first answer came when as a pupil of Vale School I joined the Girl Guides. The whole philosophy of Guiding is based on 'service to others' and disabled members were no exception to this philosophy. So as a Girl Guide I was transformed into a person who could help other people, a person with special skills. I passed tests. I had badges to prove it. Guiding paid me the greatest compliment that a child with a disability could ever have. That however severe the disability may be one could still help others. I learnt simple first aid albeit in theory, so I could instruct someone else on what to do. Margaret, then my little sister, always came to me when she hurt herself for advice on how to treat her cuts and bruises. I am thankful to the Girl Guides for developing in me the gift of self esteem. My grandmother's words have made me value my life and all its achievements all the more. It has had the effect of making me a much stronger person.

As I approached the time when I was due to leave school I became very depressed as there seemed to be no future for me. I seemed to cry buckets of tears in the privacy of my own home. For the first time ever, my parents had no solution for my future. Many of my school friends were sent to residential training colleges which seemed to be popping up throughout the country to train the disabled school leaver job skills. My teachers were very keen for me to go to the first residential grammar school for people with cerebral palsy that had just opened. I did not want to leave home. I was just beginning to walk quite well. The trauma of leaving home and taking up intensive study was a threat to my new found mobility. I was allowed to stay on at the Vale School until I was eighteen so that I could continue my physio so important for my progress in learning to walk.

After leaving school I felt I had been put on the scrap heap and there was not much going for me in the adult world. How wrong I was. I managed to build up a productive and fulfilling life for myself at my own pace, dead slow. I knocked on many doors that were slammed shut in my face. The right ones did open eventually. A few years later, I presented myself at an evening class to study for my first 'O' level which took three years to get it. When I had my five 'O' levels at about 30 years old I was told by a careers analyst that my ambition to be a teacher meant that I had unrealistic goals and advised me to sit back and rest on my laurels. His verdict was that there was no career for me in teaching or anything else. Such damnation after ten years of very hard work largely unsupported, sunk me into three weeks of deep depression and hopelessness. Then one morning I woke up to the realisation that no-one, however well qualified in disability etc., could predict my capabilities, hadn't I proved that already? From that day on I would take full responsibility for my own life and the directions I would take. I took my A levels in a shorter time, having learnt to type, and went on to get my BA Hons. at the age of 38 years. After one year of unemployment I was working!

My advice to parents/ carers of a person with a disability as you might have guessed already is to help your child develop their self esteem, to value themselves as people who have a place in society. Allow them to take responsibility for their own life, including making mistakes. Encourage your child to learn as much as possible about their disability, its cause and treatment. It is also very valuable to gain self knowledge. My parents never, in their wildest dreams, imagined me in my present situation as I described in the beginning of this article. My mother was the only person I know that never told me what I cannot do. Any fears she had on my behalf were well hidden. Often I have heard her say, "I cannot stop her, she wants to do it". And I did.

My Time at the Cerebral Palsy Unit, at Queen Mary's Hospital 1948 - 1950

Joan Ross

When my parents heard about one of the first cerebral palsy units to be opened in Britain and how successful the treatment was; they were determined to get me there as a patient. I remember being taken to see the unit one wintry day in January, when I was eight years old. I still remember the good feeling about the place. I really felt that for the first time I was among people who really understood my disabilities. Here was the largest group of children that I had ever seen that had the same disability as me and one or two had just started to learn to walk. Like my parents, I very much wanted to benefit from the treatment offered at the unit.

My parents had tremendous difficulties in getting me into the unit. There was such a long waiting list. I remember my father, a regular soldier at the time, wearing his uniform, taking me to see our local

M.P. to see if he could do anything. I was finally admitted to attend the cerebral palsy as an out patient on condition that my mother, not having any other children to worry about, and my father being away in the army, would live with me in lodgings outside the hospital. In order that I could receive treatment and schooling at the unit, my mother agreed to work voluntarily on the unit, because they were so short staffed, and the treatment depended on a one to one ratio. I was one of several children who could only receive treatment as out-patients, on these terms. We attended the unit daily for two and a half years. When I started at the unit I could not sit up without support. I left the unit at the age of eleven, able to stand alone for a few seconds. I often heard my mother speak of those days. She said that although she had never worked so hard before, she had never been so happy. My mother absorbed a great deal of knowledge about cerebral palsy having witnessed the method of treatment at first hand and being occasionally allowed to attend lectures on cerebral palsy. This is very fortunate for me as my mother's knowledge rubbed off on me and I was able to apply it to my continual struggle to learn to walk and do things for myself. I succeeded in gaining personal independence and mobility in adulthood.

My school days at Queen Mary's were very happy. I learnt to finger paint and even won a prize in Enid Blytons' 'Sunny Stories'. At this time I became interested in classical music. This can probably be traced back to the musical festivals at Queen Mary's. I can never listen to Handels 'Water Music' without remembering it played by children on their backs in bed on the beautiful bamboo pipes. Until recently, I mistook these bamboo pipes for recorders. Through renewing my acquaintance with Muriel Taylor, one of my teachers at the time, I have learnt that they were bamboo pipes. Meeting up with Muriel again after such a long period has revived many happy memories. Two of the children with me at the cerebral palsy unit have remained life long friends. They are Dorothy Anderson and John Hall.

Christina Johnson, Aged 12 in 1952

Easter 1952

Christina with Sister Downs outside D7, 1952

I was admitted to St Olaves Hospital Rotherhithe having been diagnosed as having Rheumatic Fever. I was there for two weeks, and then it was suggested to my parents that I go to a Children's Hospital as recovery was going to take a long time. Pembury Hospital in Kent was suggested or Queen Mary's Hospital for Children at Carshalton. My parents chose Queen Mary's.

I was taken to Queen Mary's Hospital by ambulance with my mother. I had a medical as soon as I arrived and was told that I would be going to ward D7. My mother wasn't allowed to come to the ward with me but was informed of the visiting times. I can remember her and myself being very upset when she said goodbye, but she promised to visit the next weekend.

I was then taken by ambulance to ward D7. I was carried into it and, at the time, it seemed to be a very long ward. My bed was at the far end of the ward in the corner. I can remember passing a row of beds on one side with teenage girls in, but the rest of the ward was empty.

It was explained to me that I had to be isolated from the other girls as I had some sort of infection. The bed was an old black iron one with a very lumpy mattress. The bedding was clean but I was not allowed a pillow, as part of the treatment was to lie flat on your back. Everything was done for me – feeding, washing, dressing. I wasn't even allowed to hold a book.

After a couple of days off the ward Sister came back from leave. Her name was Sister Downs – someone I shall always remember with fond memories.

As soon as I was clear of infection Sister Downs had me moved from the long ward to a much smaller ward called the Day Room. There I stayed for the next 15 months.

Treatment of Rheumatic Fever was rest. It was a very slow process with no medication at all. I laid on my back without a pillow for 9 weeks, not being allowed to do anything for myself. I remember being fed by the ward orderly, a very jolly lady who always made me laugh. Her name was Corra Dowding. If there was any food I didn't like Corra always got rid of it for me without Sister knowing. Sometimes Corra's daughter Judy would come to the ward to entertain us all with her tap dancing.

Every two weeks the doctor would come round to each of us in turn listening to our heart, testing reflexes etc then deciding if you could have a pillow. This went on until you reached three pillows. I wasn't always fortunate to get my extra pillows every two weeks; it took longer for me.

From pillows you progressed to sitting up ½ an hour a day which, Sister suggested, you did during lunch or teatime. After you had progressed to ½ an hour during the following 2 weeks you might be allowed to sit up for 1 hour a day. This was increased until you were sitting up all day and being allowed out of bed to go to the toilet.

I remember when I first got out of bed the other girls were quite surprised to see just how little I was. Sister Downs was there to help me. My feet crumpled up and my legs felt very wobbly. I can't remember how long I had been at Queens Mary's at this stage.

At meal times we had to sing grace before and after meals. Sister Downs would come out of her office and start us off. Our food was served on well-worn aluminium plates. The cups were too hot to handle, when you could hold the cup the contents were then cold.

There was no such thing as toilet paper; we were given a piece of brown coarse hairy sting material called tow.

When we were at the stage of sitting up for a couple of hours a day we would join in with day school. The teacher for D7 was Mrs Somerville. She was a very tall lady with short grey hair and a very deep voice. Each child had a small wooden box to keep exercise books, pencils and a reading book. Mrs Somerville would come to each bed and give us our schoolwork.

Every Friday afternoon Mrs Somerville would let us finish school early and she would read to us 'Anne of Green Gables'. It was the highlight of the school week.

When you got to the stage of your treatment where you were allowed out of bed, Sister Downs would take us out across the field to see the pigs. I think it was a small farm.

Every Sunday morning the Girl Guide captain would come to the ward and take us through preparation for working to gain our badges. When we enrolled it was quite exciting sitting up in bed with your uniform on, dress, tie and badge.

My Parents came to visit every Sunday afternoon. Visiting time was from 2.00pm - 4.00pm. In all the 15 months I was at Queen Mary's they never missed visiting once. Where my bed was situated I could see through the windows to the pathway leading to the front door and would call out to the other girls when I could see their visitors arriving.

When you were at the stage of being up from bed all day, you knew it wouldn't be long before you would be going home. When that time came it was called going up for show. You were taken by minibus to another part of the hospital with your case notes to see Dr Akassiz, who would give you a thorough medical check. If you brought your

Christina and Ernie
outside D7, 28th August 1997

case notes back you knew you hadn't passed your medical. I went up for show with two other girls and two sets of case notes came back with us. I felt sure that one of them was mine. I was very upset and Sister Downs asked me what was wrong. I told her and she showed me the case notes – they were not mine.

She said I could write to my parents to come and get me the next Saturday, although the official day to go home was always on Sundays.

I then wrote home and waited on the Saturday all packed with my coat on from early morning also wearing my new green mittens that my cousin had knitted for me. It was Sister Downs' day off that day, so I had said my goodbyes on Friday. I waited all day but no-one came for me. My mum had not received my letter but had received the official letter to collect me on Sunday.

Sister Downs was very surprised to see me still there on the Sunday. My Mum and Dad arrived Sunday morning to take me home, I remember crying because the place had been my home for the last 15 months.

My Queen Mary's Story by Brian C. Guiver

A DEEP EXPERIENCE

I was seven years old, when I contracted Poliomyelitis and became nearly totally paralysed. In particular my breathing and swallowing were very badly affected. This type of Polio is called "BULBAR". This is my story.

I first saw Ernest Earl's book, 'Queen Mary's Hospital for Children', in early 1996 whist I was in a W H Smith book shop in Sutton. The book is a historical account through words and pictures. What a good idea to keep memories alive and to share them, and to be able to read about the hospital's history and the people who worked there, together with the patients stories. The book contains a great collection of historic and modern photographs with some of the best information I have seen on the Surrey Archaeological Society's excavations on the site of the early Iron Age camp, situated in the grounds of the Queen Mary's Hospital. This has been an important site for Man, for a very long time.

I wonder if man can survive the devastation that is happening to the planet, in the form of pollution and damage to the environment etc. Whether archaeologists in about 2000 years or so time will be excavating the Old Queen Mary's site and making finds, or even reconstructing one of the old wards in situ, with beds and old medical equipment. You never know what might happen? Indeed the site will be used for several other purposes by that time? Perhaps personal records such as these may even be looked upon as time capsules of people, places and events, part of our local history?

Then later on in the year, in September 1996, I read in the local Guardian newspaper an article entitled 'Queen Mary's Unique History', which explained the background to the book along with the information that the author Ernest Earl would be at the Honeywood Lodge, which is the heritage centre by Carshalton ponds on Sunday October the 6th for a book signing event and the opportunity to meet people, who may be interested in the book.

I had already purchased a copy of the book, which I had read with great interest, and decided that I would go along and meet Ernest. So in early October I went along to Honeywood Lodge with two of my friends who I will talk more about later on. On meeting Ernest, I discovered that he was going to do a sequel to his first book. I had spoken to Ernest about myself and my experiences at Queen Mary's and he asked me if I would like to share my story. I then decided that through my own letters and thoughts I would share them in a very honest way. It made me realise that everyone's story is unique and should be recorded. I was also about to find out, how hard it is to write about yourself.

I was born in 1949, at 8, Shirley Avenue, Sutton, in an area that is known as the 'Poet's Estate'. I began school life at the age of 5 years attending St Mary's RC School, Shorts Road, Carshalton. In August 1955, the school staged a play called "Noddy in Toyland" in which I played the part of one of the robins. I can still remember going to have my photograph taken, in the small garden just outside the Head Teacher's office. As there is only about half the cast in the photograph, I have often wondered if there was another photograph taken. In those days I did not realise how important that time and event would become in my life in the future.

Time moved on and within days of the school summer holidays

in 1957, I contracted polio, through breathing in the virus from a fellow pupil who had visited my house to play. He was fortunate and only suffered flu like symptoms, but with me, it also affected my throat and caused difficulties in breathing. Initially I developed influenza type symptoms, a headache and sore throat. I was sent to bed, but quite rapidly I became very ill. The effect on me was that my whole body felt as if it was on fire, running up and down from my feet to the top of my head, and I also had a temperature of 104°f, which in modern terms is 40°C.

Our family doctor Sam Chesser was called in. He immediately gave me an injection and confirmed that I had polio and should be hospitalised immediately. An ambulance was called and I was taken to Queen Mary's Hospital, I was about to become one of Queen Mary's children. On arrival I was taken to the isolation ward and placed in a room on my own. I can remember having a lumbar puncture, and my parents were told that I might not survive that night.

I have memories of a nurse reading to me for most of that night, and a determination that I was going to fight this all the way.

A few days later I was out of the woods, but only just, and in a situation which had left me paralysed but with the ability to blink, breath, and drink. I found I could not move at all, and only just missed being put onto a respirator. If I tried to eat, it would come back again, and I have memories of this being weetabix mashed up with milk, also I was placed then back into the main isolation ward.

I can remember some of the treatments. In particular I have vivid memories of the "Hotpacks". This treatment consisted of stimulating and retraining the paralysed muscles to function by application of hot moist compresses, and by exercises. I also had a specially designed hot pack which was used for the areas around my neck, shoulder and back.

On the isolation ward when my parents visited me, all they could do was to wave at me through the glass window. My perception of this was from a totally horizontal position on what appeared to be a very hard surface instead of the conventional mattress. It was some time before they were allowed to come into the ward to visit me in person but with the added barrier of protective face masks. It was to be around 5 weeks, before I was out of the isolation ward and into the main ward, which I believe to be ward C2. During the time spent in isolation ward I was to feel very slow return of some movement in certain areas of my body.

I can remember going to the treatment ward on most days, this was some distance away which meant you were driven there in an electric van, which travelled outside in the hospital grounds and my memories are that as it was autumn time it was sometimes quite cold and so I was wrapped up in a blanket to keep the cold at bay, and I can remember being carried from the van wrapped in this blanket. At the treatment ward I had more hot baths and more exercise.

I can remember large white baths at the end of the ward and what seemed to be a bath which looked like stainless steel which seemed huge to me at the time, almost like a miniature swimming pool. This area of treatment was one I looked forward to as in the bath was a large blue and white ship with a gun at the front and, when you pressed the funnel down, the gun squirted water. This has stuck firmly in my memory to this day.

In learning to walk again I was very weak as I had lost weight and was down to about 3 stone (approximately 19 kilograms) and remember being supported by two nurses under my arms who encouraged and coaxed me to place the weight on my legs and walk. The very vague memories of that room with an assortment of children of all ages walking up and down the room with a collection of walking aids and callipers to assist them, relearning to move and to walk, I can see it in my mind's eye now.

School lessons were given on the main ward whilst in bed, or sometimes by watching television programmes. Still, boys being boys, we sometimes got in trouble, and I suppose there was a need for some discipline generally.

The television that was on our ward was sometimes watched, when the nursing staff thought we were all asleep. The older boys who were about 15 or 16 years would ask to see some programmes which I remember watching while pretending to be asleep.

When visitors gave me sweets, the staff took them away. I suppose they must have pooled all the sweets together, and I can recall the disappointment when the sweets were handed out at intervals, in much smaller quantities than we were given and I did not receive the ones that my parents had specially bought for me. This I suppose was for our own good. But sometimes I would have liked the sweets I was given as I knew they were special because my parents had brought them for me.

I have very strong memories of the fireworks display on November 5th, and the extra fireworks my parents brought in as well, which we all watched from our beds after they were pushed outside to the back of the ward. Though cold, it was good to be able to feel the fresh air and watch this colourful display.

The birthday party which was given for me by the League of Friends at the hospital on December 3rd was a special memory and all the children on the ward enjoyed and shared this with me. My birthday mail consisted of 30 letters from my school class mates. The letters I have kept until this day.

On 9th December 1957, I was also one of the children taken to see a special showing of the now classic Walt Disney 'Fantasia' at Sutton's Granada Cinema (demolished in 1980). My parents were also there with me and further strong memories exist of sweets and ice cream and a picture I had taken with the then mayor in Sutton, Councillor David Philip Thomas, for the local newspaper. The film Fantasia fascinated me, especially the dinosaurs fighting, and left a deep impression on me to this day.

Indeed the memories of this time were to instil in me things that later in life would have particular importance to me and would be part of history. It would be 1995 before I would see the film Fantasia again, this time on video, a gap of 38 years.

With Christmas 1957 looming up I was hoping that I would be allowed home to spend it with my family and friends, and I was delighted to hear the news that I would be allowed to go home on the 13th December. My time in hospital had felt like an entire lifetime to me.

My parents arrived to take me home by car, and to this day as I left the confines of the hospital I remember that I walked out of the hospital unaided. I was leaving behind me 130 days of my life that would mark forever a milestone, which the staff and my family thought close to a miracle, considering that initially the boy that was taken into Queen Mary's Hospital would not survive the night.

My return home was just before Christmas and a lot of things had changed. Life had still carried on at home, though my parents too had just ended a period of time which was very traumatic. It had affected everyone in my home, even my sister Carole. There was a new three piece suite, a piano and my bedroom had been redecorated. For me the subject of aftercare and the rules and regulations which were to be applied to my routine were about to be placed into action. They were also about to be broken by me as there were a lot of things I intended to do and all I wanted to do was to breathe the fresh air and go out and play.

I was not supposed to head a ball, ride a bike or climb a tree in fact just about everything I wanted to do. I have strong memories of the day I went out into the garden and climbed one of the apple trees, it was very hard for me but I made it to the top. A neighbour saw me attempting to climb the tree and told my Mother who acknowledged this but said "let him do it". From that day I started to do all the things I had set my heart on which included learning to ride a bike, head a ball and climb more trees.

I even managed to cycle to Brighton, and had my picture taken there just to prove it, which I have kept as a momento to this day, much to the amazement of my Mother who received a call from me in Brighton. Afterwards her comments were that she came off the phone and it dawned on her that I would now have to cycle back. The effect of that climbing and riding my bike stimulated my muscles and exercised my body. I was to cycle to Brighton three or four times before the age of 16 years. Years later my Mother was to comment that "The little patient knew best".

In between all this I regularly visited Queen Mary's for periodical check-ups. On these occasions my Father always took me which makes me recall a conversation I had with my Father in 1968, when as a young man I recall being in the back garden of my parents' home . My father spoke with emotion about the time I spent in Queen Mary's and recalled how very ill I had been, and he was told the type of polio I had was called Bulbar. The importance of this recall is that within a matter of a few years following this my Father was diagnosed as having multiple sclerosis which he had for 23 years. His ashes are in a unique grave at London Airport, where he worked for 40 years as an engineer for British Airways.

I had walked out of Queen Mary's under my own steam but with a long way to go. I was unable to hold my neck straight and it fell to one side together with my posture and gait which had been very much affected. I did not realise at that time my life had begun a circle that the events and days in Queen Mary's as one of the children would later bear a relationship with the lives of others.

My journey through the years until 1968 were filled with times when the rules and regulations applicable to early days fell into the distance as I continued to fulfil the things I had wanted to do, which assisted me as I strengthened my neck muscles and improved my posture, and it returned to normal.

Then I found myself in a situation when I was to view Queen Mary's from both sides as I commenced employment there in 1968 as a Porter, I was to work there for about 9 months and in that time it would bring me into contact with Queen Mary's children again but from a different viewpoint.

Having polio may have interfered with my education, but I have learnt so many things in different ways for one thing you learn just how precious life is when it is nearly taken away from you and learning to walk and talk again makes you very grateful for the time and opportunity to achieve the dreams you have. It is sometimes difficult for other people to understand what drives us. It is the experience of those 130 days which forever make me the person I am.

Forty years ago I was a Queen Mary's child, but my story could have been so very different from the one that I have tried to share. I have learnt how precious life is.

Thank you for sharing in my memories with me. I would like to take this opportunity to thank everyone who helped to look after me and recognise the hard work and devotion of the staff towards all the patients. The old Queen Mary's is a sad loss to us all.

Brian C. Guiver
20th April 1997

Virginia White

Dear Mr Earl

I have read with great interest your book 'Queen Mary's Hospital for Children'. My daughter, Virginia, was born at home on the morning of 8th October 1960. (Just as the chimney sweep arrived!) Unfortunately as she had a double Hare Lip and Cleft Palate (but beautiful eyes and long lashes) she was taken to Queen Mary's by ambulance on that day. My husband went with her.

At that time the wards were only given letters and numbers and no names. The Sister was a Sister Perry. In later years I was told Sister Perry went to Australia. My daughter could only be fed by a special shaped tea spoon and being a hungry baby was very good at telling us a feed was late by even a minute. At, I think four months, the hospital discovered she should be wearing a dental plate and we returned to the Dental Department where a Mr Westbrook was in charge. He was a very considerate man both to the children and parents. Once he said he was surprised my daughter did not like him considering all that he had put her through. Virginia told me that even as a baby she liked and trusted him. At four months she was the oldest of the seven babies in the country trying out the dental plates so Mr Westbrook talked about her at the World Health Conference in 1961 or 1962. Years later I heard that he had died in Australia. I think it was leukaemia.

To get to Carshalton was a terrible journey from Crawley as there was no direct train service. It was a good thing that just after Virginia was born my husband passed his driving test and that made travelling to see her a lot easier. Children were not allowed in the wards so we used to leave our son with my parents in Horsham or they came up with us.

Before Virginia's first operation we were advised to have her Christened in the Chapel but we decided against it because I felt she would come through the operations. We did have her Christened in Crawley after the first four operations.

I do hope that you continue to write about Queen Mary's Hospital. It will certainly not be forgotten by all who have had any connection with it be they patients or parents.

Yours sincerely

Shelia White (Mrs)

Lea White

Dear Ernie

Sorry I have been a long time writing to you regarding your book on Queen Mary's Hospital. It's probably all too late in any case. but at last I've managed to pop these photos in the post to you.

I was a patient at the hospital at the age of thirteen and a half until sixteen years old. I had to wear the back brace for two and half years, (until I stopped growing) for a condition known as scoliosis – curvature of the spine. I was treated in A6 by Mr Walker (one of the best orthopaedic consultants in the country, I was told at the time.

Back brace for treating scoliosis

Every fortnight during these years I would go and have the brace lengthened so as to 'stretch' me! The curve when diagnosed was 40 degrees (a sideways curve) and at the end of my treatment was only 18 degrees. Mr Polly was the technician who adjusted the brace.

I was treated at the hospital during the years 1972 to 1974. Whilst the brace was being made which took just over a month, I had to go into thick plaster of paris, which started high at the back of my head, gripping under my chin and reaching my groin. It was an inch thick and very heavy to wear. And, of course, I couldn't take it off to have a bath or wash my hair, so at the end the month, as you can imagine, I felt very dirty! I was so relieved to have it sawn off me!

I would have liked to have had the time to spend writing about my feelings during this time, and also experiences, but I would need several days to just sit and write - sorry! I do hope the book is as successful as your last and I wish you all the best.

Yours sincerely

Lea

PS. I'm Heather Whitehead's niece!

Tony Drew

YESTERYEAR

Warm summer's day, August, 1998. I'm sitting in a golf-buggy alongside the fast-flowing River Joseph. Some two hundred yards away, three-times Heavyweight Champion of the World, Muhammad Ali, sits sleeping in the afternoon sun. The Ali home, surrounded by eighty-eight acres of lush green fields, is situated in the small, but prosperous-looking town of Berrien Springs, Michigan, USA.

Sitting alongside the River Joseph (which runs through the Ali estate), my mind wanders back to the summer of 1946: It's a lovely summer day and I'm sitting up in bed, in a quadrangle situated behind Badger Close. As I recall, I'm recovering from surgery to my right leg. 1946 was my second stay at Queen Mary's. Having contracted polio in 1940, (three years after I was born), I then spent most of the war-years in the 'tranquil' setting of Queen Mary's. Ali's farm had, for me, that very same feel of tranquillity that I had experienced all those years ago as a boy growing up in a rather unique hospital.

Whenever I've read the writings of those that have been patients at Queen Mary's, there always seems to be this 'across the board' theme of, 'it was very special'. 'Very special' would invariably cover all aspects of hospital life; dedicated nursing, surgeons who gave hope or, in my case, the location itself. Unlike many other hospitals, convalescent homes and institutions, in which I stayed from 1946 through to 1952, Queen Mary's stood alone with regards to 'caring for children'!

Because of the war-years and being a member of a family that had been evacuated to Manchester, each and every visiting day, for me, was 'just another day'. Not once

The Great Muhammad Ali with Tony Drew

did I feel ostracised or lonely. On the contrary, I believe all of my inner-most strength was derived from my childhood days spent in and around the quadrangles of Badger Close.

Back on the farm, Ali and I are sitting opposite each other enjoying the late afternoon sun. Despite what many people may think, Muhammad Ali has lost none of his charisma, humour or indeed his awareness of what's happening around him. He simply has an illness – Parkinson's. And although it may affect his speech at times, he also has long periods when he can engage in conversation for hours on end – as indeed, we did.

Having discussed everything from his tastes in music, his thoughts on present-day boxing and how he came to be such a truly devout Muslim, I then asked how he thought about his being afflicted with Parkinson's. So often do I recall what this most beautiful of men replied: "It's just a test. (From God). Sure, I've sometimes got the shakes a little, but it's just a test, that's all."

I hope this doesn't come across as arrogant, but all of my life I've felt the same - 'everything' in life is 'just a test'.

From 1946 onwards, I went on an eight-year caravan of 'different places'. Some good, others, not so good. In-between 'these places', there were sporadic visits to my family (I met them for the first time in 1946), before moving on to somewhere new. Just a simple truth. It never ever troubled me to be told "I'm afraid you'll be on the move tomorrow". Like I've already said, I'd derived a strength and independence at Queen Mary's that was to stay with me - always.

Spring morning, 1990. For the first time in nearly forty-something years, I'm visiting Queen Mary's. What a wonderful day. As I drive through the hospital grounds, as if by instinct I head straight for Badger Close. (During my stay, the roads/wards were identified along the lines of B1 etc.) And there it was, my childhood home of yesteryear, exactly as I remembered it. Sure, it was closed-up, as were the adjoining buildings and yes, it was well and truly ready for the demolition gangs to make their move. But it was there. And that's all that mattered.

In life, one often hears the expression, *'you should never go back'*. As I wandered around the deserted, overgrown, still-like grounds surrounding my old childhood home, thoughts of yesteryear provoked anything but sadness. When I wrote my very first screenplay, *Guessing Days,* I described my ward as having twenty-beds either side of the ward. I wrote of climbing the 'hill' once I'd gained freedom from my bed - everything is so much bigger through the eyes of a child. The ward, as I could see, would have had no more than seven/eight beds on either side of the ward, and the 'hill'; the hill was simply a mound with a few trees on top. Nevertheless, there was a comforting smile in my mind as I climbed the 'hill' for what was to be the very last time.

Strange, but true: As I was about to leave the hospital grounds, I called in at the offices (which were somewhere near the main entrance), and a member of staff informed me that there was a collection of photographs on display in one of the (now empty) wards. Queen Mary's was apparently celebrating its eightieth anniversary.

The very moment that I walked into that ward, I knew that I was going to see a photograph of myself. What is so strange is the fact that not once did I ever recall having my photograph taken. But, and this is truly amazing, on odd occasions throughout my married life, I have spoken of one of the most vivid of memories that I could recall during my second stay at Queen Mary's - "It's a hot summer's day and I'm in my bed, as are many other patients, in the communal quadrangle at the rear of Badger Close. There's a cradle supporting the weight of my bedcovers, as I'm obviously recovering from surgery..." And this is the sole reason why that particular memory remained: "Slap-bang in front of me, two handsome young women (wearing black dresses and sporting 1940s hair styles) are standing alongside a black piano singing some song I'd often heard on the radio".

As I scanned photograph, after photograph, after photograph. My heart skipped a beat as I was confronted by the scene I'd so often described to my family. The caption above the photograph read: 'Summer 1946'. The piano-player, the two handsome singers, it was all there, together with yours truly, who is sitting up in bed with the cradle beneath his bedcovers.

I don't know if anyone will understand this. Even today I'm still kicking myself. I could have taken the photograph and said I'll return it when I've had it copied or, I could simply have asked for it. I did neither. I can only put it down to ... well, I can't explain it.

Within a couple of weeks of my visit I contacted the hospital and asked if I could have the photograph. Sadly, although I did return (twice) to search for it. It, with hundreds of other photographs, had been boxed-up and sent to who knows where?

Whenever 'I was once in hospital...' crops up in conversation, it's invariably complemented with 'God it was so, so terrible...etc.'. Why, then, is there this overall affection for Queen Mary's? For me, it will always be the tranquillity, the setting and the most peaceful of atmospheres that was created by teams of dedicated, caring people who were so very, very devoted to *the cause!*

Tony Drew

Charles Charman

It was September 22nd of 1992. Apparently it was also the Autumn Equinox. I was eight years old and had only just started in a new class in the junior school. The weather had taken a sudden turn for the worse and, like most children in my class, I ended up with an awful cold. As my mum always worked late on Monday night I had gone home with a friend. Mum came to collect me at about 6.00 pm. By 11.00 pm I was in an ambulance and on my way to Queen Mary's, Carshalton! I was having my first ever, and really quite major, asthma attack.

Mum had called in the doctor because my lips had gone blue and even dad couldn't get me to wake up properly. Before we knew it the doctor was on the phone for an ambulance. Mum says she was really scared because East Surrey Hospital had no beds and when we got into the ambulance we didn't know which hospital could find a bed for me. Lucky for me Queen Mary's Children's Hospital came to my rescue and before we knew it I was on a nebuliser and the doctors soon managed to stabilise my asthma attack.

When I woke up the next morning I was in a ward with about 12 other children. The funny thing was that in the bed opposite mine was one of my sister's classmates! The same thing had happened to her and East Surrey couldn't find a bed for her either. The nurses on my ward were brilliant and they were so kind. I remember Mum talking about the weather with them and they told her that it is quite common for people to have asthma attacks during the Autumn and Spring Equinox, when there are lots of spores and pollen in the air.

When a schoolteacher came onto the ward I looked up at my mum in horror and said "I won't have to do any school work will I?"

71

Once the doctors said it was OK for me to get up, Katie, my sister's friend, and I went for a walk around the grounds. The nurses told mum there was a special place for children to play called the Lollipop Centre. We set out to explore. I seem to remember that the hospital was a bit like a village. All the wards were in separate buildings and there were lots of little roads linking them all up.

The Lollipop Centre was quite a way from my ward. We had to cross the road and walk down a small hill. Once we found it I remember we were all in our pyjamas. One part of the Lollipop Centre had a huge conservatory and I seem to remember it being bigger than my house. There was a blue track hanging from the ceiling which had long poles with soft brightly coloured padded horses attached to it just like a funfair Merry-Go-Round. It was brilliant - mum pushed Katie and me round and round.

There were also two other special rooms. One was full of bright lights with fibre optics that were very new then. This room was supposed to help stimulate partially sighted children. The other room was full of huge blocks of foam covered with soft textures for cerebral palsy children to play safely without hurting themselves. The thing I remember most about the Lollipop Centre was a wall of water, which seemed to have a tap suspended in mid air, which had water cascading from it. I was fascinated by the tap and soon worked out that there was a clear pipe, which was almost invisible, connecting it to a water supply.

The Lollipop Centre also had its own radio station and it was broadcast around the whole hospital, so even children who were too sick to walk to the centre could listen in. I think the Lollipop Centre was a fantastic thing for children especially for those who had to be in hospital for a long time.

*Charles (left) and George on Millennium Eve
during the Nutfield Torchlight Procession*

Photograph taken by the author

GOOD-NIGHT

Sleep softly in this quiet room.
O thou, whoe'er thou art.
And let no mournful yesterdays
Disturb thy peaceful heart.

Nor let tomorrow scare thy rest
With dreams of coming ill;
Thy Maker is thy changeless friend,
His love surrounds thee still.

Forget thyself and all the world;
Put out each feverish light;
The stars are watching overhead,
Sleep softly then, good-night!

NURSES' STORIES

These wise words of the Desiderata were pinned up in the office of A2. I regularly read them. *EE*

DESIDERATA

Go Placidly amid the noise & haste & remember what peace there may, be in silence. As far as possible be on good terms with all persons. Speak your truth quietly & clearly & listen to others, even the dull & ignorant; they too have their story. Avoid loud and aggressive persons they are vexations to the spirit. If you compare yourself with others you may become vain & bitter; For always there will be greater & lesser persons ... than yourself. Enjoy your achievements as well as your plans. Keep interested in your own career however humble; it is a real possession in the changing fortunes of time. Exercise caution in your business affairs; for the world is full of trickery. But let this not blind you to what virtue there is. Many persons strive for high ideals & everywhere life is full of heroism. Be yourself. Especially do not feign affection. Neither be cynical about love, for in the face of all aridity & disenchantment, it is perennial as the grass. Take kindly the counsel of the years, gracefully surrendering the things of youth. Nurture strength of spirit to shield you in sudden misfortune. But do not distress yourself with imaginings. Many fears are born of fatigue & loneliness. Beyond a wholesome discipline, be gentle with yourself. You are a child of the universe no less than the trees and the stars. You have a right to be here And whether or not it is clear to you no doubt the universe is unfolding as it should. Therefore be at peace with God. Whatever you - conceive Him to be & whatever your labors & aspirations in the noisy confusion of life, - keep peace with your soul. With all its sham & drudgery & broken dreams, it is still a beautiful World. Be careful. Strive to be happy.

Found in Old St Paul's Church. Baltimore, dated 1692

"The chamber of sickness is the chapel of devotion."

QUEEN MARY'S HOSPITAL FOR CHILDREN
THE FIRST SIXTY YEARS

It was July, 1886 and feeling ran high in the village of Carshalton for it had become known that the Metropolitan Asylums' Board had purchased a park of some 136 acres from the Westcroft Farm Estate on which to build a convalescent fever hospital for children from the various London parishes.

The park lay in the southern and most beautiful part of the parish on the Surrey Downs and the ground rose to an area known as Stag Field, for in former days a large statue of a stag had stood at its highest point, a reminder of the days when deer roamed freely in the district and the Earls of Derby had owned the land. It was only later that this was to prove of minor interest compared with that which was aroused by the uncovering of the considerable neolithic and iron age settlement lying hidden beneath the ground where the Hospital East and West Blocks now stand.

But, one might ask, why did the Metropolitan Asylums' Board buy an estate so far from the centre of London for this purpose? Memories are short and probably few of us know how very acute was the problem of treating children suffering from infectious diseases and whose homes were in large towns and cities. The children most at risk were those from the vastly overcrowded slum areas and most of these, even before contracting one of the infectious fevers, were undernourished and badly equipped to deal with any actual illness. Accommodation in the existing hospitals was very limited and many children had to be discharged before they were fit and well.

In spite of these considerations only two things appear to have been important to the villagers of Carshalton – the fear that the hospital would spoil the amenities of the district and that there would be a great risk of infection from the ambulances carrying the convalescent patients through the village to the hospital, - and so it was that a great protest meeting was called, (was it in the Public Hall, already twenty years old?) Representatives of the Board attended the meeting; the villagers' fears were laughed to scorn and the building plans went ahead.

By 1902 the buildings were complete but they were no longer required for their original purpose for quite unexpectedly one of the group of river hospitals at Dartford had become available and so, in Carshalton, the hospital stood unused and untenanted for several years.

It was in 1908 that the Local Government Board became seriously concerned about the plight of sick children in the various London Infirmaries where no special provision was made for them and they were cared for alongside adult patients, often elderly or dying, and so it was that they appealed to the Metropolitan Asylums' Board to undertake the care of such sick children who were suitable to be moved from the overcrowded infirmary wards into the much healthier country air. The Board were ready and able to comply with this request for there stood the needed hospital ready and waiting on the Carshalton downs.

Immediately the Board set to work to find a suitable Medical Superintendent and their choice fell upon Dr. W. T. Gordon Pugh who was charged with the job of equipping the hospital and recruiting staff. So successful was he at these tasks that on 29th January 1909 the hospital, then known as The Children's Infirmary, was officially opened by John Burns on what he described as "the breezy downs of Surrey". Very quickly the need for the hospital became only too apparent and in 1912, in an attempt to ease the pressure on the beds, verandas, each containing thirty beds, were added to ten of the ward blocks.

As soon as the hospital was opened the training of Sick Children's Nurses was begun, but what was life like for the probationer in those early days? Let us look for a moment at what one of the first of them has to say about conditions then.

"There were about thirty of forty of us probationers, I was almost the junior and we stood very much in awe of the seniors and were expected to open doors for them and offer them our chairs; we filled one long table in the dining room. Each ward block had a general trained staff nurse in charge and there was one sister in charge of each street. They lived in the staff blocks and had a maid, sitting room, bed and bath room. They were very grand people and we made up a rhyme about them:-

Who are the ladies of stately gait,
Who live in almost palatial state,

76

Waiting a man to be left by fate?
THE SISTERS.

These were very different days and I could tell you many interesting things about them. We certainly got a very good training as we had to do big dressings, splints, extensions, etc., which in most hospitals were done by doctors.

We had 1,000 children, all from the London slums, during the First World War, many of them starving and tuberculosis in the worst stages, with dreadful dressing with plugging etc. to be done. Dr. Pugh liked them to be renewed four hourly and with thirty two children, nearly all with dressing, I had over one hundred to do daily, so three of us were kept busy running around with the dressing trolley."

What a contrast with the wards today.

1911 was Coronation year and the hospital was accordingly renamed Queen Mary's Hospital for Children. In 1914 Queen Mary became the patron of the hospital and on the 14th May 1915, Her Majesty graciously visited the hospital.

Pressure on accommodation continued to be severe and this was made worse by the fact that with the post-war reduction in working hours, some of the wards had to be used as dormitory accommodation for the staff and to provide a hospital chapel and so, in 1928, a further major enlargement was begun. This consisted of a large nurses' home arranged in four wings around a central kitchen, dining rooms and serveries, two double ward blocks and a chapel.

In 1930, as a result of the Local Government Act of 1929, the hospital passed to the control of the London County Council who therefore opened the extensions.

From its very early days, Queen Mary's Hospital had become a famous centre for the treatment of children who needed more than a few weeks in hospital, and so many did in those pre-sulphonamide, pre-antibiotic days. Protections against many diseases was minimal and then results of such conditions as bone and joint tuberculosis, osteomyelitis, poliomyelitis, rickets and juvenile rheumatism were extremely sad to behold. And so it was that large units were developed here for the treatment of these very things. This work continued unabated until the outbreak of war in 1939.

One of the most important landmarks in the story of the Hospital was the opening of the school in 1912. At that time many of the children were patients in the hospital for many months and even years and Dr. Pugh became very worried about two things – they often had nothing to do and some of them were growing up completely illiterate and so, using his powers of persuasion, he prevailed upon the Board to appoint three school teachers.

What a revolutionary idea. Who had every heard of patients in hospital having lessons and certainly occupational therapy was unheard of. But Dr. Pugh won the day and so the country's first hospital school was begun, eventually to expand into the full service provided for the children today and to be the pattern for all those which followed in its wake.

There are so many developments which have taken place at Queen Mary's Hospital that it is difficult to pick out those which warrant special mention but a word must be included about the treatment of Poliomyelitis.

For many years, children suffering from the acute stage of the disease had been treated at the Western Fever Hospital but with the treatment available at that time, they were left with many deformities which required corrective operative surgery and so, in the middle of the 1920s it was decided to set aside some forty beds for the treatment of these children. It was soon realised that much muscle re-education was also necessary and so in 1927 an outdoor, heated treatment pool was constructed for underwater exercises for these patients.

In 1937, Miss Elizabeth Kenny was given every facility to demonstrate her methods of treatment here. The results were shown to be much better than those obtained with orthodox methods and so Queen Mary's Hospital became equally as famous for its treatment of children suffering from poliomyelitis as it had been for many years past for the care of those suffering from various orthopaedic conditions, including tuberculosis.

It was the work of Dr. Pugh in designing his well known spinal and hip carriages which helped to keep Queen Mary's Hospital in the forefront as far as the treatment of bone and joint tuberculosis was concerned – ably assisted by the men working on the actual making of the various surgical appliances. But conditions were changing and so the story of the Hospital must move ahead.

A few days before the outbreak of war in 1939 we had to hurriedly discharge many of our more convalescent patients in order to admit others acutely ill from the London Hospitals and very soon after this the verandas had to be withdrawn from use, thus reducing the bed capacity from 1,284 to only 1,000. Certain members of the trained nursing staff, who were members of the reserves of the nursing services of the armed forces, were called up and many adjustments had to be made. But they were made and the work of the Hospital continued although not quite along its usual lines.

Gas masks were issued to all the staff and patients alike, that is, all those beyond the period of infancy, for those for babies were not yet ready and thus it was that one poor junior sister, working on A6, had to climb up and down a ladder numerous times, carrying a bucket of wet plaster of paris with which to block up all the ventilation holes in the ceiling and floor spaces in a room which now forms part of the Committee Room. The intention was to place all the babies in there if there was a warning of a gas attack before the baby helmets were ready. Mercifully the room was never needed but it was the best preparation which could be made at the time. The plaster of paris has remained to this day but is now rapidly falling out of the spaces in the ventilators.

It was the autumn of 1940 that the first bombs fell on the Hospital and very soon such incidents became common. (It was Sir Alan Daly, Medical Officer of Health for London, who subsequently told us that we had the doubtful distinction of being the most frequently bombed L.C.C. Hospital.) Material damage was not inconsiderable but, because of the scattered nature of the wards, personal injuries were slight and until 1944 the work continued as usual.

But the patients were changing. A1 and 2 were now acute surgical wards and a unit for the treatment of vulvo-vaginitis had been transferred to Queen Mary's Hospital from a special hospital in London while the ground floors of the Hospital Blocks were housing adult patients suffering from bone and joint tuberculosis. With the introduction of rationing at the outbreak of war rickets had almost disappeared, it would seem, almost overnight, for the mothers took and gave to their children all that was available on the ration books and this included cod liver oil. The work of infant welfare clinics had spread far and wide and so far fewer marasmic babies were being admitted. It was at this time that we first admitted children in the acute stage of poliomyelitis.

June 1944, the tide seemed to have turned for the allied forces when suddenly, after a lull in the raids, in the early hours of the morning of the 13th, the sirens began wailing again and before five o'clock there had been three short alerts; nobody knew why, for nothing had happened but two days later, of all times on Magna Carta day, the fury of the V1 Flying Bombs, (Doodle bugs) burst upon us. Many of them never reached central London for both the fighter planes and the barrage balloons were out to intercept them and great was the excitement amongst the children. The staff were not so happy for they could see the added danger to the patients in their care and every day there were many alerts. At length, on one particularly bad afternoon as far as flying bombs were concerned, experts visited the Hospital and ordered the immediate evacuation of the patients. Naturally the staff thought that this was the result of the afternoon's events – little did they know of the government's fear of what might happen should a V2 rocket fall on the Hospital.

And so it was that a few days later, at around five o'clock in the morning, there passed up the drive and into the grounds, a procession of Green Line Coaches, suitably converted into ambulances, to take the first large contingent of children to the ambulance train which would carry them to Durham. The day staff were already on duty and the children awake and prepared for the trip. What a long day that was but the staff accompanying the children rose to the challenge and eventually every child was comfortably tucked up in bed before those caring for them sought their own temporary quarters and a well earned rest.

This pattern of events was to be repeated twice as other large groups of patients left for Yorkshire and Devon leaving but those in one small special unit to travel only as far as the northern outskirts of London. What was left? A children's hospital without children and so it was to remain until after VE Day still many months ahead.

The following year a return to Carshalton was possible and great was the rejoicing among the members of the staff, many of whom had been scattered in a variety of hospitals, only a proportion having been evacuated with the children. Gradually the Hospital filled up again but not to its pre-war numbers for several of the wards had been damaged beyond repair and only about 840 beds were available for use.

Very quickly it was realised that new problems had arisen. There were many young children with unrepaired congenital defects because of the continual movement of the population during the preceding years; there were many babies, mostly the children of American service men, who were suffering from congenital syphillis as their fathers, treated with the new drug Penicillin, had been told too quickly that they had been cured, and there was an outbreak of diptheria to be dealt with. Accommodation was still further limited by the fact that we also had to accommodate well babies from a war time nursery when the premises which they were occupying had to be returned to their owners.

Further changes were in the air. Now not only were the sulphonamides available for the treatment of many diseases but Penicillin had been released for civilian use and very quickly the picture began to change. For the treatment of many diseases, children were in hospital for a far shorter time. Then came another breakthrough, the anti-tubercular drugs and this, coupled with the heat treatment of milk, rapidly changed the picture of tuberculosis as treated in the hospital. Eventually protection against poliomyelitis became the order of the day and so fewer and fewer beds were needed for children suffering from this disease.

Meanwhile in July 1948, the Hospital had been taken over as a Single Hospital Group by the National Health Service under the South West Metropolitan Regional Hospital Board; as a London County Council Hospital it had served London only, but now it became the children's hospital for the immediate surrounding area, and for many from further afield and very quickly provision was made for the full range of modern paediatric services for an increasingly large area.

But the new drugs and the greater care all round for the child in the midst were beginning to bear fruit and so it was that, although more children were being admitted to the hospital than before, there were many empty beds as the children quickly recovered and were discharged home. How good for the children, but the staff hated to see the many fine facilities only partly used.

It was in July 1958 that the terrible news was received that the Ministry of Health proposed to close the Hospital for sick children and then use it to house mentally handicapped children from the Fountain Hospital at Tooting. Immediately the Management Committee decided to fight this decision. They were ably backed by the League of Friends, the Surrey Education Committee's Medical and Special Schools' Committee, and from many other associations and private people throughout the world, so that within a short time some 41,000 people had signed the petition against closure of the Hospital. These were worrying but stirring times without knowledge of what the outcome might be.

Eventually in the light of continuous pressure, the Ministry made its decision; Queen Mary's Hospital was to continue to treat the sick child but approximately 340 of the beds were to be used for the care of mentally handicapped children. And so it was that on 1st October 1959, the two individual Hospital Management Committees were dissolved and the new Fountain and Carshalton Group Hospital Management Committee set up in its stead in order to develop at Carshalton a comprehensive children's hospital for both mentally handicapped and physically ill children. The new group consisted not only of the two main hospitals but also of the South Side Home, The Turret, Osborne House, Ellen Terry Home and Brooklands, subsequently St Ebba's Hospital, which had previously cared for the mentally sick patient, was redesignated as a hospital for the handicapped and became a member of the Group.

Why you may ask were all these changes necessary? For an explanation we must take a short trip to Tooting.

It was in 1893 that a 'temporary' hutted Hospital was opened at Tooting for the treatment of infectious diseases. This was the Fountain Hospital and the word "temporary" was hardly the correct one to use in connection with its buildings for they continued to serve the public in a variety of ways for nearly seventy years. It was here, in its early days, that Edith Cavell started her nursing career.

The story of the Fountain Hospital is a chequered one for in February 1911, no longer being required for its original purpose, it became the temporary home for a number of older, "feeble-minded" girls transferred there from a special school. This particular use, however, was short-lived and in February 1912, it was opened as a Hospital for "unimprovable imbecile children" and so it was that this hospital, which in its early days had performed yeoman service in the treatment of patients suffering from infectious diseases, was now to become famous as a pioneer in the care and training of severely handicapped children.

For many years the staff of the Fountain Hospital continued to work with their patients in poor, overcrowded conditions in "temporary" buildings of the standards laid down during the latter part of the last century and one can offer nothing but admiration for the results which were achieved in such difficult circumstances not only directly in the care and training of the children but also in the field of research into the causes of mental handicap.

At last it became abundantly clear that something must be done about the conditions at Tooting and also the site was required for other purposes and so it was that the Ministry of Health began their search for alternative accommodation. Quite quickly their eyes were directed towards Queen Mary's Hospital, this was understandable in view of the number of empty beds here but to suddenly and completely cut off the services to the sick child was not so easily comprehended.

The compromise decision having been reached by the Ministry of Health, the first wards were quickly prepared to receive children from the Fountain Hospital and indeed they arrived before Christmas 1959. Gradually more wards were prepared to receive children from the Fountain Hospital until in 1963 it was finally closed, the patients having been admitted here or sent to St Ebba's Hospital, and now opportunity was really ours to develop as a comprehensive Children's Hospital.

On the paediatric side of the work, as well as the general medical and surgical wards, there is a large spina bifida unit and a busy isolation department; the casualty and outpatients, splint and physiotherapy departments are all busy places, the orthopaedic work is extensive and the ear, nose and throat department increasing its work while the muscular dystrophy, cerebral palsy and long stay medical units fill a much needed want. The emotionally disturbed child is also catered for, as are those requiring ophthalmological and dental treatment. The pre and post-operative ward has in fact become an intensive care unit kept busy by the work carried out in the theatre suite.

Amongst the handicapped children, much thought and care is given to their training and they have certainly benefited in health by their move to the cleaner air of Carshalton and the fact that here they are cared for in much smaller units; those who are disturbed or who have physical handicaps are given particular care as also are the autistic children and of course, if they become physically ill, the full services of the paediatric wards are instantly available to them.

Much more could be written about Queen Mary's Hospital: Mr Pastry's Pool which is such a joy to the patients; the Zoo, the special work of the two schools for the physically sick and the mentally handicapped children, each with its special job to do, but space does not permit anything but a passing reference. One thing however must be commented upon. Queen Mary's Hospital always allowed the patients to be visited but for many years this was only once a week as far as parents were concerned. It is very doubtful whether many could have afforded to come more often; but even in those days members of the local Toc H visited the children regularly week by week, and guiding and scouting (not forgetting the brownies and cubs) were features of every ward where the children were old enough to take part in such activities.

Free visiting is of course a fairly recent development, but a very much appreciated one as are the rooms in E Staff Block in which relatives can stay and the flatlets which were such a wonderful gift from the Jewish Aid Committee for Mentally Handicapped Children.

Throughout the years, the training of nurses has continued without a break and now Queen Mary's Hospital can offer not only the full three year courses in paediatric or handicapped nursing but also an integrated course in children's and general nursing and post-registration courses for both the children's and handicapped registers maintained by the General Nursing Council while a pupil nurse course in the general field is now in being.

As one looks back over the years, all honour must be given to those who have gone before and shown the way, but this alone is not enough if it does not inspire those who are following in their footsteps to make their contribution to the care of the children in the hospital even better in the days to come.

Muriel Hayman

Former Nursing Tutor
Muriel Hayman
pictured at her Carshalton
home on 17 September 1993

Joyce Bradford (née Watkiss)

Christmas 1924

What a long driveway I thought as I trudged up it with bag and baggages to start my training as a probation nurse at Queen Mary's Hospital, Carshalton, Surrey. I was eighteen in 1925, just out of school and although I knew I wanted to look after sick children I had no idea whether I was going to manage! However we were taken in hand by Sister Mac, the Home sister—firm but kind—strict on etiquette and behaviour—"a nurse must never run, dearie, dearie" and so on.

We were issued with a grey dress plus cap, apron, white sleeves which buttoned on to short sleeves of a dress (taken off for work but marks off if not on for meals or taking Matron around the ward!) We also had a cardigan and a thick cloak—the latter invaluable if one worked as far as C or F Streets in all weathers.

We were to have £40 a year during our training period of three years. It had to go a surprisingly long way but with a five shilling postal order sometimes from home which was welcome! Shoes were the problem but we found crêpe soles were the answer. The boys on C8 dubbed me Nurse Kipperfeet.

There opened up now for me a world of bed-pans, keeping children clean and dry, free from bed-sores, making beds—the corners of which had to be right or Matron on her rounds would pull all the bedclothes

1926

85

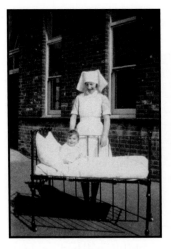

1930

out and give a black mark! No doubt I'm a better person for having to tow the line! We were never allowed to stand still and were put to cleaning windows, brasses and other scrubbing. Harsh discipline, which has mostly disappeared now, the pendulum having swung the other way. Doctors were waited on hand and foot— sisters at their elbows handing them each thing. Now my doctor tells me he's hardly noticed when he walks in!

We had evening classes with Sister Tutor; Anatomy, Physiology, Hygiene, Nursing also special diet classes in the kitchen. The children coming from mostly poor homes—malnutrition was rife—their bodies had to be built up to struggle against diseases—no National Health Service at that time! Yet visitors used to arrive with all sorts of cakes, sweets etc. irrespective of diets. They thought these were their treats—they were up to a point.

Tuberculosis was the major disease of my time there but Dr. Pugh was well away with his light treatment, fresh air and an all-round diet. I remember Joe calling for children going to different departments— light treatment, physiotherapy and to be fitted with callipers (metal support for weak or tubercular legs) or those carriages for tubercular spines. I don't remember the children complaining. Perhaps it was in spite of all they had company but they did enjoy shouting at each other and us!

We had a wardful of lovely quins at one time all suffering from pulmonary tuberculosis. Not many survived but good plain food helped them along. Prunes and custard on Sunday were the highlight of the week. Shouts of "It's pruins, nurse, it's pruins!"

Hilda Williams (L) and Joyce Watkiss (R) 1930

86

After the days work which included two hours off either morning, afternoon or early evening as we worked until 8 p.m., the tennis courts were available—that was if you hadn't thrown yourself on your bed! We made up quite a good team and played matches notably against St. James Hospital, Balham.

Every child admitted had to be thoroughly examined. A lot of them had nits—these were treated with a sassafras oil—this was applied on bandages to make a sort of cap on the head and usually did the trick.

I still remember Dr. Pugh—a fine figure of a man. There was a lady doctor—Dr. Thawson—a dedicated woman who sadly died of T.B. Sister Thallard—bottom picture page 127 in your first book. Sister Eustace on the left of the picture—page 118—both dedicated to Queen Mary's.

After passing my examinations I left Queen Mary's to take up my general training at the Middlesex Hospital but during a break I met my husband so that did not materialise! I went back to Queen Mary's as a Staff Nurse—£60 a year now!—leaving to marry a year after.

*Joyce in 1998
at Hyde Heath,
Buckinghamshire*

Sister Elizabeth Kenny

A King, A Prince and a Little Child

On 4th April of our Australian autumn, in 1937, my niece, Mary Farquharson, and I boarded the Orient boat, Otranto, at Brisbane. Saying farewell to my aged mother had not been without its pang, despite her cheerily voiced happiness in my opportunity to go forth and seek help in my life's work.

Mary Farquharson, a studious young girl, had already proved herself an excellent technician. This daughter of my elder sister was greatly excited at the prospect of her first trip abroad, especially since it was in the nature of a mission.

Friends had filled our cabins with beautiful Australian autumn flowers. The last coloured streamer from the ship's rail broke fluttering away, and the Oranto set out on the first stage of its long journey. At Sydney Harbour the rest of our party joined us, the little patient, her mother and her five-year-old brother, the children's nurse, and Miss Helen Grant, a second technician who was trained in the method of treating long-standing cases of infantile paralysis and cerebral diplegia. Mr Y— had left on an earlier boat.

While the voyage was breath-taking to the two young Australian girls who were leaving their home land for the first time, to me it was haunted with memories a quarter of a century old. At Adelaide, I met a former cruise companion, Sister Ella Morphett, a little more matronly but as sweet-faced as ever. At Perth, I found another good friend of the war transport days, Sister Eileen Kiernan, whose sparkling wit and pretty, ruddy hair showed no change. Both were astonished and a bit sad, I think, to see what the years had wrought in my own appearance. My hair was almost snow-white.

By way of the Suez Canal, we eventually arrived at Southampton. Then by car to Chislehurst, the home of Mr and Mrs Y—. The road, in this English May, wound through a countryside that was lovely with copper beech and yellow blossoming laburnum, with great spreading carpets of bluebells. Reservations had been made for Mary Farquharson and myself at the Hyde Park Hotel, in London, while the second technician remained in the village with the Y— family.

A short time after our arrival we received a call from my cousin Michael Kenny, my father's namesake, the middle-aged bachelor who was now the owner of the centuries-old home in Ireland. He had become a distinguished scholar and linguist, and held a high government position in London. His warm efforts to make us feel "at home so far from home" were not without amusing incident. Mary and I had left the hotel and found accommodation with Miss Ann Ellison, of Maida Vale, London, and to these quarters Michael brought us one evening a fine gramophone which he shyly protested he had no further use for. That we might while away lonely hours, he also brought some Australian songs. In his eagerness to show us how it worked, poor Michael began to open it at the wrong end, and it was quite clear to us that he was opening it for the first time. In the kindness of his Irish heart he had gone out and bought the gramophone, records and all, and brought it to us as a "cast off" gift. Although he was visibly flustered at being found out, he enjoyed equally with the rest of us Peter Dawson's singing of "The Sea Road" and the recordings of John Cormack.

There was a pleasant interval of some days during which we cooked our own meals and ate them under the sycamore tree in Miss Ellison's back garden. Here Michael Kenny sometimes joined us. Fancy how over-whelmed we were when one evening he brought us gilt-edged invitations to attend a garden party at Buckingham Palace as guests of Their Majesties King George VI and Queen Elizabeth! Cousin Michael turned to my niece Mary and asked how she liked the idea of attending a royal garden party.

"Thank you, I do not mind," said Mary simply.

"Moira!" Michael exclaimed, using the Irish form of her name. "What did you say? You do not mind? Do you know there have been people waiting for twenty years for such an invitation? You have your invitation after only a few weeks in England, and yet you casually say you 'do not mind'!"

We had to enlighten him. In Australia the phrase is used to express deepest gratitude.

We spent the next few days selecting our garden party hats, frocks and gloves. Mary looked charming in her maize-coloured lace gown and the hat she had chosen to go with it. As for myself, I afterwards read an account in an Australian paper which stated that, "Sister Kenny was smartly gowned in black relieved with flesh-pink touches and a hat to match." That particular hat finally went on an adventure of its own. After my return to Australia I was visiting my clinics in New

South Wales, at the Royal North Shore Hospital and at Newcastle. On the train between Newcastle and Sydney, I carefully placed the hat, covered with tissue paper, on the rack above the seat I was occupying. It was a hot day, and I opened the window. Whisk-out went the hat! Worn at a Buckingham palace garden party, it was last seen sailing over the trees of the Australian bush.

The garden party was as colourfully impressive as we had expected it to be. I had often passed by this home of England's monarchs, but had never dreamed that one day I would enter its wrought iron gates or walk down its great hall. The hall led down to the terrace, and the garden was beautiful with greensward and flowers on that sunny June day of 1937, before enemy bombs had brought their ruin.

The King came into the garden alone by one door, while from others appeared the Queen and the little Princesses Elizabeth and Margaret Rose. The gracious charm of the royal family's reception of their subjects from every quarter of the realm was most stirring to me, and I found myself wondering if the majestic Dowager Queen might not be looking wistfully back to the days when her husband had stood in the place now occupied by her stalwart son. And what were her thoughts of that other, her eldest, Edward, now so far away from her side? It was not many years after that bright June day that Queen Mary was to lose her youngest son, the handsome Duke of Kent, in another World War. She could not have been aware of that as she stood with his lovely young duchess on the dais under an awning, greeting the throngs that came by. Heartbreak is not reserved for the commoner alone.

Among the peers and peeresses, the rajahs and maharajahs and ranees glitteringly present that day, one will be forever memorable to me as the most exquisite representative of the human family I have ever beheld.

She was a young girl from India, who wore a pale rose-pink sari within the shoulder folds of which nestled two live moss-rose buds and green leaves. Her costume set off to perfection the smooth beauty of her raven hair, her lambent, long-lashed dark eyes, and her fine, creamy skin with its blush-rose tint.

All too soon the fascinating garden party came to an end, the guests went away, and the guards in their splendid uniforms closed the gates.

It had been my intention upon leaving Australia to present myself for a "check-up" by a cardiac specialist in Harley Street. But since the good doctor had died two months before my arrival, there was nothing for me to do but let my heart go unattended, and I promptly forgot about it in the work I was called upon to do.

Mr and Mrs Y— were most anxious to get the work started in England. The medical man who had treated their daughter before their visit to Australia again examined the child and was delighted with the progress that had been made. He insisted that I meet his colleagues who had specialised in this field, and made appointments with some of the senior men in London. But here again the medical men ran true to form. Their response was remarkable for its lack of enthusiasm.

The days were slipping by, and I would soon have to return to Australia. Before leaving, however, I had to make existence secure for the two technicians who were remaining behind for the full period of two years, in keeping with the conditions under which they had been brought to England. Inured as I was to the devious methods of bureaucracy, I was more or less prepared for the red tape I was to unravel before I could sail for home.

First, my two technicians must have permission to operate from the Director of Health of the L.C.C. To prepare the way I interviewed the Agent General of Queensland, Mr Pike. Mr Pike was most gracious, and immediately got in touch with his department. Both he and I were surprised when we were told that the Director-General of Health, Sir Frederick Menzies himself, would like to see me next Saturday, at 10.30. Needless to say, I was flattered, especially when we were told that it was not Sir Fredrick's custom to visit his office on Saturday morning. Mr Pike was eager to hear the outcome of the interview.

A day or two before the Saturday appointment, a member of Parliament, originally from Australia, invited me to afternoon tea on the terrace of the House of Commons. After delicious strawberries and cream, he showed me around the historic building, and explained many of its age-old traditions, such as the one barring His Majesty the King from entry into the House of Commons unless special permission was granted.

Our visit to the House of Lords, which was in session, was particularly interesting, because the retiring Prime Minister of England was receiving an earldom on this day. My host family pointed out the huge pile of buildings on the bank of the Thames—the County Hall from which orders are sent forth that influence the lives of more people than there are in Australia altogether.

It was on the fourth floor of this building that I was to interview the Director of Health the following Saturday. I arrived a little early and wandered along the river bank, looking up at the huge pile whose solid substance seemed intended to outlast eternity.

At the appointed hour I made my way to the entrance and inquired for the office of the Director-General of Health. After walking what seemed to me like miles of corridor, I was at last ushered into the room of the secretary of Sir Fredrick Menzies who escorted me to his office. Sir Fredrick received me cordially, and suggested after our talk that it might be wiser to attach my small unit to some county hospital where other technicians might observe the work and learn it. I agreed to his suggestion but added that Mr and Mrs Gardner, the parents of the child we brought back with us from Australia, were financing the technicians and must also agree to the proposal. That same afternoon, at an informal meeting, this initial problem was solved in a satisfactory way.

The next step in the procedure, that of going the rounds of the London Country hospitals to see which one would be the most suitable, was grimly humorous to me. I was amused at the anxious haste with which poor Dr Topping would hustle me off the premises of a particularly hostile hospital. I was amused, but I was still thinking of the children—and in crippled children there is no laughter. At length we came to Carshalton, in Surrey, the most ideal spot for a hospital I have ever seen. A long avenue lead to the administrative building. The avenue was flanked by flowering trees and a well-kept hedge on either side. the wards were placed at intervals in the grounds, each with its courtyard of greensward and beautiful shade trees. The walks, or "streets," between the wards were hedged with flowers and clumps of lilac bushes with, at intervals, an archway of roses to add their touch of beauty to the settings.

Before undertaking to set up my work at Carshalton, I thought it advisable to present some of the motion-picture evidence of the results that had been achieved in Townsville. Dr Mills arranged for the projection of these films in a room at the British Medical Association buildings, in Tavistock Square, London. Several prominent doctors attended the showing, and evinced keen interest in what they saw. Dr

Topping announced that his chief, Sir Fredrick Menzies, had had a visit from Sir Robert Wade, of Australia, and Sir Robert had suggested that my theories would be most interesting to investigate.

In a short time Mary Farquharson and I were settled in the handsomely appointed nurses' home at Carshalton, where I was allotted a suite of rooms with a maid, and my niece was given a very comfortable room to herself. A ward in Queen Mary's Hospital was set apart for our work.

Two early cases were admitted from the Western Hospital at the end of their isolation period. Both were affected in the arms, one less severely than the other. Both had a certain degree of contraction even at this period. While one was to remain with a rather severe residual paralysis of the left upper arm, the second patient recovered completely in a month. My niece had taken over a very attractive child who had been a victim of the disease for three and a half years. Beside these, the little daughter of Mr and Mrs Gardner visited the clinic daily.

Except for a brief rest holiday in Ireland, Mary Faruharson and I devoted ourselves unremittingly to the work at Queen Mary's. Presently the first ward allotted us was full. A second was prepared, and then a third. It had been arranged that the patients should be filmed on their admission and from time to time thereafter, in order to record their progress. Teaching the staff, answering correspondence, demonstrating to visitors and attending to the filming of the patients constituted for me a full-time job.

Visitors came from all parts of England, and from other countries. Naturally argument was rife among them, and there was considerable bewilderment at the presentation of what amounted to a revolutionary approach to the treatment of infantile paralysis. Dr Swartz, of Paris, telephoned one morning to ask aid for his little daughter, who had contracted infantile paralysis several weeks before. The distracted father had summoned all the foremost medical men in Paris, until their number amounted to eighteen. The verdict was that the child would never walk again. Dr Swartz crossed over from France that same day, and after I had explained my methods and demonstrated on some of the patients, he requested me to visit his daughter in Paris.

The next day I arrived in Paris by plane. After examining the pretty little French girl, I concluded that our treatment would enable her to walk again, at least, but that she must remain under my supervision at Carshalton.. As the child, the idol of her parents, could not speak a word of English, the separation would be keenly felt, but Dr Swartz seized on this last hope of her recovery, and she was duly admitted to our ward at Queen Mary's. Dr Swartz's confidence in us, I may say, was ultimately vindicated.

During my short stay in Paris I visited the World's Fair, a most impressive testimony, indeed, to civilisation's progress. Within a couple of years, that civilisation was to enter upon its supreme test. Perhaps one might have foreseen the inevitable in the symbols of Russia and Germany as they opposed each other on their respective sites. The huge human figure surmounting the Russian Pavilion, the bold, straight column with its swastika floating defiantly from the top of the German Pavilion—both towering above their neighbours—were outstanding landmarks.

Back at Queen Mary's again, I was happy to see our work progressing. The little French girl was placed in a bed beside a small, dark-haired Armenian, whose mother had taught her to speak a bit of French. The vivacious miss from Paris soon had all the ward singing or attempting to sing nursery rhymes of her own language. It was most amusing to hear the little cockney children putting forth all they had to keep pace with the nimble little Parisian.

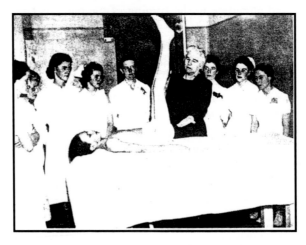

Sister Kenny demonstrates her revolutionary
treatment of Infantile Paralysis

My presence in England had been given considerable publicity, and appeals had been coming in from the different countries abroad. My next visit was to Poland, in response to an appeal from Frederick Zielinska, the governor of the University of Warsaw. His young daughter, Wieslawa, had fallen victim to infantile paralysis three years previously and had received the best treatment the continent of Europe had to offer. After studying the history of the case, I did not think the child's prospects would be bright, but when a final urgent plea was accompanied by a return ticket from London to Warsaw by air, I felt that it would be more humane to go than to refuse.

In the early autumn of 1937, I left Croydon aerodrome for Warsaw via Berlin. In the latter city, air schedules were so arranged that travellers would have ample time to take in the sights between a change from one plane to another—and incidentally spend a little money, I suppose. I was content, however, to partake of a light luncheon and watch the passing show. Planes left frequently for all parts of the world. An announcer called out the departure and arrival of each plane. Without confusion, passengers found their way to the platform they sought. Planes taxied into place, travellers got on board, and with a minimum waste of time or effort, transfers were made. The Nazi machine had reached an astonishing degree of efficiency.

At the Polish border, after I had produced my passport and was returning to my plane, I was suddenly confronted by an agitated customs officer who could not speak English. I listened intently while he tried to sneeze something that to me was utterly incomprehensible. A young Polish gentle standing near by gallantly came to my rescue with these words: "Please madam, he say follow his backside to the desk table!"

Keeping a straight face, I followed. My passport was re-examined, I was asked how much money I was taking with me, where it had been minted, and what was my errand in Poland. The letter I produced from the governor of the University of Warsaw cleared the air at once. The English consul at Warsaw would be communicated with immediately, and all would be well.

At the landing field in Warsaw, I was met by Mr Zielinska and an interpreter, a Miss Jacque. After we had tea, they drove me through the city to the wrought iron gates of the university campus, within whose precincts the Governor had his home. Here I was introduced to the family whose history is one of the most tragic I have ever known.

This was Madame Zielinska's second marriage, the interpreter informed me. She had previously been married to a White Russian and during the revolution had fled from her home with her husband and their two-year-old child. They were standing at the railway station with other refugees anxiously awaiting the arrival of the train, when the child slipped from the platform in front of the locomotive. The father jumped immediately to save the child, and both were instantly killed. Friends helped the prostrated woman into the train, and she was taken over the border into Poland where for days she lay between life and death. The shock had brought on a miscarriage, but after a time the kindly Polish people who had given her the comfort of their home saw her strength returning, though tragedy lingered in her eyes and in the swath of snow-white hair that reached from her left temple to the nape of her neck.

During her illness and convalescence a constant visitor to the house was Frederick Zielinska, the governor of the great Warsaw University, whose sympathy was deeply touched by the experience of the young widow. When time had softened her grief, she accepted him in marriage, and when the union was blessed by the arrival of a blue-eyed daughter, years of happiness seemed to lie ahead. The happiness came abruptly to an end just a decade later, when their adored child became crippled with infantile paralysis. There followed an endless search throughout Europe for some one who could restore power to the young limbs. Eventually Wieslawa Zielinska was brought to our clinic at Carshalton.

My visit to Poland was a memorable one. The city of Warsaw was beautiful with palaces and statues of famous men who had been born in that heroic land. Old Warsaw with its square where people met in the evening to exchange gossip; the leisurely drives through the streets by horse and carriage; the excellent food produced in homes and in restaurants: the generous heart of Poland itself reflected in the hospitality of her people; the quaint custom of never permitting a guest to pay for his purchases when he went shopping—these are only a few of the memories that remain with me still.

On the eve of my departure, the Zielinskas, with Miss Jacque accompanying us, took me to a café where a prominent Polish conductor was requested to have his orchestra play some Polish folk-songs for my entertainment. Although the words were unintelligible to me, I was deeply touched by the plaintive strains of the music, and profoundly grateful to my host for asking to have the old songs played. I was flattered by the lengthy account of my work which appeared in the press, but even more so by the friendly gesture of the conductor of the café orchestra, who sent his musicians to the aerodrome to play farewell on the morning of my taking leave.

During her stay at Carshalton, the little Wieslawa Zielenska mastered English to a remarkable degree. The following is an excerpt from an article which she wrote for a Warsaw newspaper:

AMONG THE PARALYSED CHILDREN AT QUEEN MARY'S HOSPITAL IN CARSHALTON

CARSHALTON, in June.

I am one of the sick children treated by Sister Elizabeth Kenny, who invented her own method of relieving the after effects of infantile paralysis. Besides the English children there are also patients from Italy, China, Germany and Australia …

It is 11.00 a.m. The morning exercises in the hospital have begun. The patients are treated under the personal supervision of Sister Kenny, who is assisted by other specially trained nurses. They take good care of the children, go with them through their exercises, baths and treatments. There are 43 children in my department.

Sister Kenny is greeted joyfully by all the children. She talks to all of us, says a few kind words and smiles. She treats us all with sympathy and tenderness which can be seen in her eyes, whether it be the little curly-headed Italian, pretty as a picture, a pale boy looking sadly and motionlessly in front of him, or the slanting-eyed Chinese girl with the charming smile on her delicate mouth. Sister Kenny wishes to help all unfortunate sick children by her own methods....She offers the priceless gift of health to poor paralysed children.

Small babies of a few months and older children, even boys and girls of up to sixteen years of age, are wheeled in their comfortable beds from the dormitory into a very large and sunny room. The treatment takes place there, and its beneficial results are often seen within a short space of time. Children who suffer from inertia of their limbs at birth are also treated by a slightly different method.

The treatment is neither tiring nor painful. Simple exercises, bath, water therapy, all suitably applied ... Sister Kenny said to my mother and me, as her only patient from Poland, "If anyone should be interested in my method in Poland, I am prepared to teach him or her free of charge, so that the children and people suffering from infantile paralysis could be treated in their own country instead of abroad, where they often do not feel happy and it is detrimental to the progress of their treatment. Obviously it would be necessary for a person desirous of learning this method of treatment to have knowledge of anatomy and of the English language."

The damp and foggy English climate does not suit me very well, and I wish I were in Poland with my own people.... All my leg muscles are already much stronger, especially around my knee and in the foot.

Sister Kenny is going back to Australia shortly, probably at the end of August. It is to be hoped that somebody will interest himself in her method of relieving the after effects of infantile paralysis, and that he will bring it from England to the poor Polish children.

WIESLAWA ZIELINSKA.

What eloquence can be compared with the simple words spoken from the heart of a child? In a short time I received letters from doctors, nurses, even from "quacks," asking my permission to come to England to learn the work so that they could take it back to Poland. The medical authorities at the hospital refused to grant their requests, however. Six years later, when I was at work in the great Middle West of the United States of America, another appeal reached me from Warsaw's Dr Przeworski:

Due to undernourishment and bad hygienic conditions, various epidemics are spreading in an alarming way, among them infantile paralysis.... Would it be possible for you to give a detailed description of your treatment to the physicians abroad so that they could apply it to help others? I sincerely hope, Sister Kenny, that you will do your utmost in this matter. You have already saved many lives—now you have a chance to save many more.

Wieslawa Zielinska and her devoted parents? Oh, yes, I heard what happened to them, from a refugee friend of theirs. Their bodies were removed from the ruins of Warsaw University, and the shadow of the swastika hurried my cortege....

And They Shall Walk

IV

Resolution

Extending thanks and good wishes to Sister Elizabeth Kenny
Resolved by the City Council of the City of Minneapolis

WHEREAS; many sufferers from infantile paralysis have been
released from the fear of spending the rest of their lives as cripples due
to the work of Sister Elizabeth Kenny, and

WHEREAS; the Kenny method of treatment for infantile
paralysis will save many more from this same fear, and has conferred
a boon upon humanity, and

WHEREAS; Sister Kenny has graciously chosen Minneapolis
as the place to carry on her work and the City's reputation as a centre
of healing has been increased thereby not only in this country but
throughout the world,

THEREFORE BE IT RESOLVED THAT THE CITY COUNCIL
OF THE CITY OF MINNEAPOLIS extend to Sister Kenny its deepest
thanks, and its warm hope that she will be granted many more years to
carry on the great work she has unselfishly dedicated her life.

Passed April 9, 1943   (Sdg.) W. Glen Wallace
President of the Council
Approved April 9, 1943   (Sdg.) Marvin L. Kline, Mayor
Attest   (Sdg.) Chas. C. Owanson
City Clerk
Members of the Minneapolis City Council

Secret New Cure
Nurse's "Miracles" Helpless Cripples Made Well

The People, November 7 1937

SPECIAL TO "THE PEOPLE"

Prominent doctors and London County Council officials sat in a darkened room at Queen Mary's Hospital, Carshalton, a few days ago watching a film flicker across the screen.

They saw pale-faced kiddies, pathetic little victims of infantile paralysis lying helpless in bed—and then, the bloom of returning health already in their cheeks, the same children toddling to and fro.

At the end of the film one of them turned to a woman who had sat in the audience.

"Splendid, Sister!" he said. "Carry on the good work!"

Several months ago Sister Elizabeth Kenny came to England from Australia with a new system of treating infantile paralysis which, she claimed, held the secret of a permanent cure.

Medical experts at first sceptical, became interested when they learned that she had refused £20,000 for her secret.

"I don't want to make a profit?" she said, offering her services free to the London County Council.

They decided to give Nurse Kenny an opportunity to prove her claims. A ward at Queen Mary's Hospital, Carshalton, was set aside for her use. In every bed was a hopeless case—a helpless little invalid whom the doctors said would never be able to walk.

A film was taken in the ward. Three months passed. Another film was "shot." The two were shown to doctors and L.C.C. officials a few days ago.

AN EXTENSION

And, as a result, "Nurse Kenny's Ward" is to be run for another nine months.

She modestly refuses to discuss the secrets of her system, but I understand that brine baths and exercise play a large part in it.

While many doctors declare that absolute rest is the only treatment for infantile paralysis she believes in encouraging the patient to move as much as possible, so that new strength and vigour flow into cramped muscles.

Some of the children under her care are already beginning to toddle. In a few more months they will be well on the way to complete recovery.

"It is too early to give a definite decision as to whether the treatment will be given in other L.C.C. hospitals," an official said yesterday.

"But the progress Nurse Kenny's patients have made during the last three months has been so encouraging that her system is to be continued for another nine months."

Nursing Is Her Career

MISS JOYCE PACKHAM, eldest daughter of Mr. and Mrs. R. Packham, of Claremont-place, Snatts-road, Uckfield, is enjoying a week's holiday after passing the final of her examination at Carshalton Children's Hospital. She took up nursing just over four years ago, and is now studying to qualify as a registered sick children's nurse. She is not yet 21.

Miss Packham loves her work, and she told the "Express-Herald" that her hospital specialises in the Sister Kenny treatment for poliomyelitis. At Christmas, 1952, Wilfred Pickles broadcast from Carshalton Hospital, but Miss Packham missed it because she was on duty at the time.

Cutting from the 'Express-Herald'

Nursing Is Her Career

Miss Joyce Packham, eldest daughter of Mr. and Mrs. R. Packham, of Claremont-place, Snatts-road, Uckfield, is enjoying a week's holiday after passing the final of her examination at Carshalton Children's Hospital. She took up nursing just over four years ago, and is now studying to qualify as a registered sick children's nurse. She is not yet 21.

Miss Packham loves her work, and she told the "Express-Herald" that her hospital specialises in the Sister Kenny treatment for poliomyelitis. At Christmas, 1952, Wilfred Pickles broadcast from Carshalton Hospital, but Miss Packham missed it because she was on duty at the time.

Reminiscences

This is said to be a sign of old age, but things are changing so rapidly these days, that it is a good thing to look back - sorry for the good things that are past, glad for the bad things that are no more.

I started my nursing career in a children's convalescent home, filling sand bags in September 1939 and have a wonderful photo of me in uniform - cap down to my ears and no hair showing, longish dress covered by a white starched apron. We had a day off a month then and took home two pounds a month. My day started at six a.m. when I had to rouse and "pot" all the toddlers. Their bedroom was directly underneath the matron's bedroom and woe betide me if one of them cried! They were washed and dressed and breakfast at was at seven a.m. - after which we had ours! We did all the mending of children's clothes whilst we supervised them at play. We were allowed off duty from two p.m. to four p.m. and back on for tea, or off duty six p.m. to eight p.m. The day ended by again taking the children up for "potty round" and so to bed at 10 p.m. Once a week we had to give a mug of liquorice mixture to every child on this night round for the good of their 'souls'. It reminded me of the poem: "Who took me from my warm, warm cot, and put me on the cold, cold pot, whether I wanted to or not - my mother!"

The treatment for a child with convulsions was a steam pack, using bed sheets wrung out of boiling water and mustard baths were often used.

1940 saw me commencing my training for sick children and a very happy four years they were at Queen Mary's Hospital, Carshalton, Surrey. They were bungalow wards, stretching along streets A to F. All the children were nursed out of doors all the year round and we all became very hardy. Spinal carriages and hip frames held the T.B. children, plasters encased limbs with osteomyelitis - the latter had to be nursed out of doors and the plasters covered with deodorant bags which failed to disguise the smell of suppuration - in the very early days when Penicillin was in its infancy and was not used prophylactically.

The air raids started and we watched the sky glow red as the fires of London lit up the night. We took our turn at fire watching - there was just one building of three storeys and we kept watch from the roof top. I remember sharing the watch with the battle axe of the Sisters and it filled me with amazement to find she was human and sang " Don't sit under the apple tree with anyone else but me"!! On duty she expected us to polish floors and tables with a big heavy bumper until the woodwork shone and reflected the sunshine of our rosy faces - we almost had to LIFT the beds CONTAINING the patients, sixteen year old boys in hip spicas etc. - over the polished floors out into the courtyard.

Rations were the order of the day and each week we collected our sugar and butter rations in our labelled glass jars. A large dining room contained long refectory tables and up at the top table sat Matron and her minions looking down on us from the heights. I revisited not long ago and now there are small tables with dainty tablecloths on each and no Matron hovering over the gathered throng.

The Chapel was a lovely building and had a choir gallery and we had a good choir and enjoyed singing for the services. The Christian Fellowship was held weekly and we had wonderful times together. I well remember one night we had stayed up talking to 10.30 p.m.(!!) and on returning to our room found all the corridor lights had been turned off - night sister had done her rounds. I had to feel my way along the walls and if I met anyone, they would have thought I'd had one over the eight! - but as I had my Bible under my arm, I knew I was safe.

On night duty we were alone on our wards but had a colleague on the adjoining ward. The doctor on duty always did a final round at about 11 p.m. and on one occasion a nurse found a message on her desk in front of her - "nurse and patients all sleeping well". Although it was a training school, most of our patients were long-term and not acutely ill on many of the wards. On my first night duty I remember not feeling very well - very nauseated and shivery and sat huddled over the open fire, which we kept replenished through the long winter night. Night Sister came round and in a real Irish brogue said "Tis the night duty my dear". So I plodded on, cared for the children, cooked breakfast - porridge and bacon and eggs for all twenty six of them - and eventually crawled off to bed. I awoke at four p.m. and looked in the mirror and have never seen such a deep shade of yellow staring back at me. So into sick bay I went - next to the kitchen where all the savoury smells wafted out to me, as I was restricted to my fat-free diet.

The time came for me to go and do my "General" and I went to Kingston County Hospital.

I was nearly side tracked from my S.R.N. training by a Tutor who offered me a post as nurse/attendant to a mentally disturbed lady travelling to America. It would have been good money and quite an experience, but I'm glad I finished my training - glad I achieved my Silver Medal in those difficult days, glad I did my 'Midder'.

The years have passed by. I finished my Nursing career a Nursing Officer for Health, caring for the nurses resident in our varied Nurses Homes, both medically and spiritually as the need arose, having time to talk and listen, such a rare commodity these days. I didn't push my Christian faith but knowing I couldn't have coped in all these situations without it. I have had many happy years as a paediatric ward sister both at St. Helier Hospital, Carshalton and at the Royal Devon and Exeter Hospital here in Exeter, followed by six years as Assistant Matron at our local Geriatric hospital. All have left memories, mostly happy, some sad, but great fun to reminisce.

(I retired in 1983)

Anon.

Marjorie Burnell

Doodle-bug Fire at Queen Mary's

I started at Queen Mary's as a Student Nurse in September 1943 at the princely salary of about £2-12-00 (£2.60) per calendar month, after a month in the P.T.S (Preliminary Training School) we started work on the wards attending many of our continuing lectures during our off duty.

After about six months we went on to night duty for spells of three months at a time, and during that first spell of night duty the Germans started sending over the first V1 rockets (doodle-bugs). When the first one arrived everyone was mystified and didn't know what they were. We soon learned and over the next few months saw plenty.

At that time night nurses slept on the top floor of the nurses' home and it wasn't unusual to look out of the window and see a doodle-bug going by only slightly higher than the window. Provided the engine was still going you were safe but once the engine cut out you watched it very carefully to make sure it wasn't heading your way. Several did, in fact, land close to the Hospital (the surrounding area being one of the more seriously affected parts) but the Hospital itself wasn't hit.

In the event the doodle-bugs were getting rather too close for comfort so the Hospital was completely evacuated. As many children as possible were sent home and the majority of remaining patients and staff went to either Westerham or Knaresborough. I was one of the comparatively few nurses and patients who were still at Queen Mary's and remember early one morning just before coming off duty a V1 fell at the back of Wards F7 & 8. The engine had cut out and I was changing the draw sheet of one small boy. I sat him down on the floor with the readily available wet sheet over his head! I thought better that than he be showered with debris and glass.

A few days after this the rest of us were "evacuated" to the North Eastern Hospital in St. Anne's Road, Tottenham. It was hardly evacuation because within a few hours, before we had got our bearings, there were incendiary bombs on the Hospital and Nurses Homes, so there we were in a chain passing buckets of water.

After taking my preliminary state examination, I went to Knaresborough with a few other nurses from Tottenham but before we went the V2 rockets started to arrive. Yorkshire was so peaceful after London.

Finally, the war in Europe came to an end and we all returned to Carshalton. The Nurses who had remained in Tottenham were the first back and they helped preparing the wards for the return of the patients.

Marjorie Burnell

Prinia Riordan

Once Upon Awhile at Queen Mary's Hospital - There lies a tale in Prinia's Nursing Story

In my childhood my mother retold stories of her nursing days at St. Giles Hospital, London and when she was in the Colonial Service in Ceylon and Nyasaland (now Malawi), Central Africa. I listened, absorbed and knew, that one day, I too would train as a nurse.

Prinia Macpherson 1953

On leaving school in South Africa, my father, knowing my keen interest in nursing, chose the hospital as to where I would train. How he knew about Queen Mary's Hospital for Children remained a mystery. However, he made such a good choice; perhaps he had read about the treatments being pioneered there.

In 1953 at the age of 17 years, I left Nyasaland and travelled to England to be with my Aunt, until October of that year when I went to Queen Mary's Hospital for Children. I started off as a Junior Trainee, until such time I reached the age of 18 years to start my nursing training. My first day, in my white uniform dress with blue epaulettes, was spent

Julie, aged about 1, at QMH in 1953

on a ward under the charge of Sister Fraser. I remember my first work was in the sluice room dealing with bedpans and dirty laundry. I don't know who was the most surprised, myself or Sister Fraser, that I managed to do the job!

Sister Fraser's ward was a surgical ward specialising in congenital defects. Whilst on Sister Fraser's ward I became quite attached to a little girl, about 1 year old, Julie who came from Wales and had congenital bowel defect. Her parents found it difficult to visit regularly and she was a long stay case.

On my afternoons off, I would take Julie out to the nearby field,

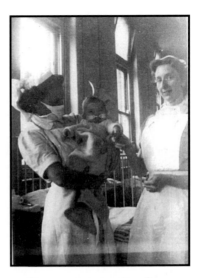

*Prinia Macpherson
with Julie*

*Two nurses caring for a
baby with a Hare Lip*

behind the ward and spend time with her. I took many photos of Julie and sent them to her parents, so that they didn't miss out on her growing days. Later when she was transferred to Great Ormond Street Hospital in London for further surgery, I visited her. On her return home to Wales her parents very kindly kept in touch for a while.

I helped to look after babies with Hare Lips and Cleft Palates, feeding them with a special spoon so that the milk didn't spill and they were able to swallow as best they could. Special nursing care was given to these babies after the operation and the DB (Denis Brown - I think this is what it was called) splint strapped into place, so that the lip was held in a good position.

Once a little boy, Ivan, came in with a double thumb on one of his hands. I learned to nurse children with bat ears and children with other

Sister ... and Sister Ling

107

Prinia Macpherson and Mary Sainsbury on the steps of the Nurses' Home, QMH

congenital defects that needed corrective surgery and nursing procedures before I began my nursing training.

I started my nursing training on 30 June 1954, first going into a 3 month Preliminary Part One Training. We had 4 tutors, Miss Hayman, I remember well, teaching us Anatomy and Physiology. Miss Hayman always wore her brown uniform dress, and Miss Grubb who taught us nursing procedures had a grey dress uniform. There was also Sister Ling (Betty) and one other Sister. I kept in touch with Betty Ling for many years, whilst she was in Perth, Australia, until her death in the mid 1980s. I enjoyed the Preliminary Part Two training and the surgical and medical block training we had during the course of our three year training, with many other girls. Some names I can remember - Shirley Cornish (now Evans), with whom I have kept in contact all these years and enjoyed Shirley and Ralph's New Zealand visit in 1996. Other names come to mind, Jean Kearney, Pearl Corner, Mary Sainsbury, Ann Amons, Margaret Tribe, Angela Treadwell, Alison Clements, Betty Wedgebury, Pat Collins and Berys Smith (now Lamplugh), living in Canada with whom I also kept in contact.

1st year nurses in the June 1954 Part One Preliminary Training with Sister Ling and Sister ..., with Alison Clements sitting in front

A page from Nurse Prinia Macpherson's book showing the practical instructions having been recorded.

SECTION I

Ward Management:—
- Ventilation
- Heating and lighting
- Methods of cleaning and care of:
  - sanitary annexes
  - kitchen
- Care and cleaning of:
  - furniture
  - bedding
  - bed cradles and other accessories
  - mackintoshes

General care of patient:—
- Admission of patient
- Care of patient's clothing and valuables
- Bathing in bed
  - in bathroom
  - infants
  - children
- Care and cleaning of:
  - mouth and teeth
  - head and hair
  - hands and feet
- Care of pressure areas
- Lifting and moving patients
- Care of unconscious patients
- Preparing meals
- Serving meals
- Feeding helpless patients
- Feeding infants
- Feeding children
- Treatment of:
  - infested patient
  - infectious patient

SECTION I (continued)

General care of patient—(continued):—
- Taking and charting:
  - temperature, pulse, respiration
- Bedmaking:—
  - general bedmaking
  - making children's cots
  - special modifications for:
    - admission of patients
    - operation/s
    - cardiac diseases
    - pulmonary diseases
    - fracture/s
    - plaster
- Filling and placing hot water bottles
- Use of: water pillows or air pillows
  - electric pads and blankets
- Giving and removing bedpans and urinals
- Observation and collection of specimens of and disposal of:
  - urine
  - faeces
  - sputum
  - vomit
- Measuring and charting fluid intake and output
- Giving and receiving reports on patients' condition
- Administration of drugs:
  - giving medicines
  - giving hypodermic injections
  - storage of drugs
- Inhalations:
  - steam kettle
  - steam inhaler

109

One thing I particularly remember about Preliminary training is being asked to write an essay on psychology. Faced with this daunting task, and not really knowing what was required, I duly wrote a few pages. To my surprise when the results were given, I had done very well and acquired a high mark. We had a book in which our practical instructions and experiences for the certificate of nursing sick children where recorded. Also recorded were our date of entry and an Index number, mine being 135812.

At the end of our three year training we received our certificates and I was delighted to have been presented with a silver medal, along with two other nurses. Angela Treadwell was presented with a gold medal. Beatrice E. Dowell, the Matron of QMH was one of the presenters.

Queen Mary's Hospital for Sick Children Certificate

I had a very happy time on the wards - care of Gastro Enteritis babies coming in so ill and Sister Carter, saying how quickly they go down, but they recover just as quick. We had one little baby, Jilly, who was very ill on admission and put into an oxygen tent. Seeing her pull through was indeed a miracle. When the babies were recovering their cots were wheeled out into the courtyard so they could enjoy the warmth of the sunshine and fresh air.

One time, whilst on Ward F5, there was a shortage of nurses due to winter ills and there just weren't enough nurses to bottle feed all the babies. Sister Carter and I being the only ones on duty for that part of the day, prepared the feeds; the babies were then supported by a pillow, and the bottles given to each baby. We would walk around the cots at a brisk pace, making sure the babies were feeding, getting their wind up and settling them down again. We changed their nappies and saw to the needs of the babies needing specialised care, then started the rounds all over again.

Jilly, recovering from Gastro Enteritis, on ward F5

The next ward I trained on was ward C1, the orthopaedic ward, under the charge of Sister Froude, with the patients on spinal frames and the care of paraplegics. It was on this ward I became attached to a little baby of three months, Catherine, who had a congenital dislocated hip and needed to go on a frame. I made her smocked dresses with open backs. She was the dearest baby and it was such a joy to see her gradually progress from the frame into a plaster cast, then walking, over a nine month period of time.

When my three months were up on the ward I remember becoming very upset at having to leave and Sister Froude telling me not to become so involved with the patients. I couldn't help but return from time to time to visit Catherine. To my delight, later I returned to the ward for a further three month spell.

Whilst working on Sister Froude's ward one grateful father insisted on taking or photo and presenting the staff with a copy. He

Two Staff Nurses on Ward F5

111

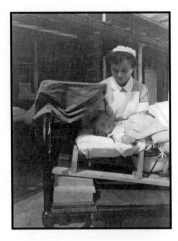

Prinia Machpherson and
Catherine on Ward C1

Ward C1 - the Ward
Orderly and Mary, the
Ward Maid, with Catherine

wrote on the back of the folder, "In appreciation of your very kind attention to Wendy Cartwright, Queen Mary's Hospital for Children, June 1995".

The ward orderlies and maids were a great help to the new nurses on the ward, showing us where things were kept and helping over tricky situations with the children. Their encouragement meant a great deal. In particular I remember Rose and Mary.

Being on duty in the winter time, especially working on the wards where the children slept on the verandas, were cold nights. I well remember the little cuddly rugs the children had. The long wards with sleeping children and a fire at one end made a cheery sight. When we lit the fire, in order to help the fire to get going, we used a dash of the liquid floor polish!! One of my experiences was with a small boy who had Haemophilia. He had bitten his tongue and it wouldn't stop bleeding. I spent most of this one night applying pressure to the tongue with a Stypven pad. This was one time in which it was a hazardous job, for he bit my finger in trying to be helpful.

In the years between 1955 and 1957 I was working on Ward D10 under the charge of Sister Kemp. On this ward there were older girls of 14-16 years with varying disorders related to Rheumatism and Rheumatoid Arthritis. The girls were great fun and I particularly remember Chris and Theresa. It was on this ward that, perhaps, the

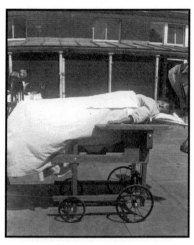

Patient on a spinal carriage
on Ward C1

Young patient on Ward C1
and Wendy Cartwright

Nurse Prinia Macpherson
and Staff Nurse Sheila Monk

Staff Nurse Sheila Monk,
Nurse Prinia Macpherson,
Nurse ..., Sister Froude
with young Linda on C1

*Chris and Theresa
on Ward D10*

Ward D10

psychology paper I wrote and the contents helped me with these older girls, who had to be very still in their beds in the early stage of Rheumatism, helping them to cope with the Cortisone therapy they received, giving them the moon shaped face.

On this ward, as on others, we did four-hourly treatment of the pressure points, first rubbing the children's heels, elbows, bottoms and backs with soap and methylated spirits, then drying, powdering and settling them back into bed making sure the bed spread was straight and kicking in the wheels of the beds, so that the ward looked tidy.

Another thing I remember is when we had to clean up any small child after the toilet session, or any toilet accidents, we used "tow". This was something that looked like it should have been used for mattress stuffing. This must have been very uncomfortable for the children but it certainly did the cleaning job.

Visiting times were greatly looked forward to by the children. The doors opened and hardly a moment passed before the parents eagerly found their children. Once the two hours were up, on some wards a bell was rung, or we would go around saying that visiting time was up.

Queen Mary's Hospital was famous for the work Elizabeth Kenny did for the children with Poliomyelitis. I only did a short spell on this ward, but my friend, Alison Clements was a Staff Nurse under the charge of Sister Nicholson. I visited the ward to take photos.

As a Staff Nurse I did a 3 month duty on ward A 3 - Theatre. I really enjoyed my time here, under the guidance of Sister Ling. The surgeon, Mr Nixon, would whistle or hum while he was operating ; I remember one tune being 'Greensleeves'. The days on Theatre were very busy laying up trolleys, sterilising and cleaning up the Theatre after operations. Just before the children went into Theatre, whilst the Anaesthetist carried out preparations, I told the children stories to keep their minds off what was about to happen and comforting them. I well remember the excitement of being

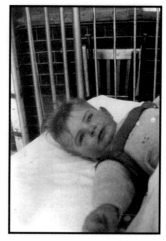

A young polio patient

called out at night and on occasions being left in charge. Usually we were called out for an appendectomy.

Each year we had a fete day; what excitement for the children. Their carriage frames were pushed into the field decorated with balloons and many of the children wore pretty bonnets. One year comes to mind with Cal McCord, the cowboy, being the guest of honour and taking the children for rides on his horse.

Fete Day Celebrations

Above - more fete day celebrations

*Right - Cal McCord with young
patients on Fete day*

The Nurses Home, situated behind the hospital chapel was huge, with a long corridor from the entrance of the nurses home, passing by the Sister's dining room and a larger dining room for the nurses and a shop where we could buy essentials and some luxuries. The large airy sitting room was always a nice place to meet our friends, watch T.V. and relax. On the floors above, we had our own bedrooms and there were tea making facilities in the kitchenette. Doris Coulsdon was always there for us at the Nurses home, giving encouragement or comfort if need be.

One of the things we liked to do in our evenings off, was to visit a café in Carshalton Beeches where they served ice-cream with the

The Hospital Chapel and Nurses Home

116

most delicious hot chocolate sauce. We were mindful of being back and walking through the Lodge Gate before 10pm ... that is if we didn't have a late pass.

I left Queen Mary's Hospital in 1958 to return home to my parents in Malawi and to have a holiday, before I started my General training at St. Batholomews Hospital in London. They recommended I had a years holiday and put on some weight. I married in 1959, so never did my General Training. We emigrated to New Zealand with our children in 1970 and live in Motueka, a horticultural area at the top of the South Island.

Prinia Macpherson

Presentation of the Medals

Nurse Betty Wedgebury, Matron Beatrice E. Dowell, Angela Treadwell, ..., Nurse Prinia Machpherson, and Nurse ....

OCTOBER '56 P.T.S. FINAL BLOCK

There once was a class, of the dimmest, of girls!
In spite of their lipstick and pretty pinned curls.
Attractive, but sleepy, they sit on their chairs,
Their faces wear various, vacant, stares.
Nurse Bleach is watching the workmen pass by,
I wonder who uttered that terrible sigh?
As Cam bites her fingernails, Sal sucks her thumb,
Nurse Rawlings expression is terribly glum!
Miss Hayman pops questions, but just what it means,
What happened to Queen Victoria's genes?
An ominous silence, why, nobody knows!
She wore them out cycling, we all suppose!
Nurse Baker is busily drawing some trees,
Nurse Smythe is trying, so hard, not to sneeze.
This wretched hay fever! just when will it go?
What is Miss Grubb saying? I would like to know.
Nurse Evans is listening, thank goodness for that,
If she knows the answer, I'll eat my hat!
Nurse Acott, as usual, sits good as gold,
Miss Hayman tells stories, incredibly old,
We have heard them at least twenty times before,
I suppose it won't hurt to hear them once more!
They say that variety's the spice of life,
Oh, what was that word beginning with 'Kyph'?
Or, what did it mean? if I only knew that!
I have not even got the brains of a gnat!
Miss Hayman would say I don't use what I've got,
But, of course, as you know, that is absolute rot.
Miss Grubb swats flies, or tries, should I say,
As the fly inevitably gets away!
How boring it is, just to sit up and sigh,
While the time is passing, so slowly, by.
"Oh Nurses! the windows," Miss Hayman implores,
So we open them all, including the doors.
"It's terribly hot, it's a stifling day"!
We all sit and shiver but not a word say.

Then in comes Miss Grubb for a lecture at two,
And closes the windows, without more ado.
Again comes Miss Hayman, reluctant we rise,
To go and prepare our trolleys and trays.
"Nurse Thomas, lay up for a turpentine stupe."
"Oh dear, no," she says "now I'm in the soup!
I haven't a clue what to do, so you see,
There is really no point in your asking me."
Nurses Acott and Bleach must make Mrs Brown's bed,
Should they start from the bottom, or is it the head?
If only she were a more elegant shape,
And it's not so polite, to just sit and gape.
Nurse Morgan lays up for a subcut, she thinks!
Jan looks at Sheila and solemnly winks.
A tepid sponge, three times, for Doreen,
I don't really think she is terribly keen!
But to learn these things, I suppose we must try,
If we didn't laugh, I'm afraid we would cry.
Oh, here comes a wasp, a treacherous thing,
I hope, to goodness, its not going to sting,
Let's hope Miss Hayman keeps out of its way
We don't really want her to die today!
Well, now, I must really complete this tale,
Or else in my, duty to you, I would fail.
The exam days came and slowly dragged by,
And at times we all felt we would willingly die!
But, at last, the results were up on the board,
And each one was accepting her due reward,
Just fancy that! Well, what do you know!
Of course, we've all passed, I told you so!

GEORGE HEATH – Nursing Tutor

(These are his memories)

From 1962 – 1965 I was the Charge Nurse on A4, a pre-operative ward and was given a free hand. Under the influence of Miss Jones it became a major modern centre of surgical excellence in many specialities. Miss B. Ling had a tremendous influence.

The surgeons were Messrs Nixon, Forest, Eckstein, Orton and Bushell. Mr Westbrook was the dental surgeon along with Mr Thomas and others. Dr Manford was one of the anaesthetists.

In 1965 I was transferred to the School of Nursing to work with Miss Hayman, Miss Grubb, Miss Saunders, Miss Dennison and others.

From 1966 to 1968, I attended a course at Queen Elizabeth College, University of London in order to qualify as a registered tutor.

In November 1970, I left Queen Mary's to be a Tutor at the Ivy Long School of Nursing, West Crawley, Sussex.

On St Luke's Day, 1964, I became engaged to Sister J Beaumont and was married on 1st May 1965 by Mr Nauman, the Hospital Chaplain, with a Special Licence from the Archbishop of Canterbury. We were the first couple to be married in the Hospital Chapel. Miss Patrick gave us an excellent reception.

During these years, social life at the hospital was good, but 'duty always came first'. There were Christmas and pantomime rehearsals with Charles Cryer and Arthur Houghton. Who can forget them?

One would think that modern paediatrics started within the last 10-15 years if one took notice of the media. In 1962 (unless there were very special circumstances) ORAL administration of pre-medications was the norm at Queen Mary's and the children never left alone at all. The Sister's office was converted to a Play/Mother room and this is where oral pre-medications were administered.

Every child was observed continually and the fullest records of their clinical condition monitored and seen to be monitored. No child was left in discomfort – in fact before a child recovered from anaesthesia an injection of analgesia was given – thus pre-empting pain and distress. Cleanliness was of the highest order. I wonder whether 'Multi-Resistant Staphyloccus Aureus' would be so prevalent now if such attention was given to basic cleanliness in our working environment.

Great tribute must be paid to those in charge of the wards who received their own children back following the operative procedures. Their dedication, organisation of the wards and detailed post-operative long term care had to be seen to be believed.

The first wedding in Queen Mary's Chapel, 1st May 1965

Nursing Tutor George Heath married Miss Jocelyn Beaumont, Sick Bay Sister for Staff

The ceremony was conducted by the Rev. D Naumann.

Queen Mary's Chapel was ordained by the Archbishop of Canterbury for the solemnisation of marriage.

CONDITIONS NURSED ON B4

The following article gives some insight into the knowledge, skill and care asked of a nurse. They are only to be admired.

WARD OBJECTIVES

WARD B4 - NEO-NATAL SURGICAL

The unique function of the nurse is to assist the individual, sick or well, in the performance of those activities contributing to his health or recovery that he would perform unaided if he had the necessary strength, will or knowledge. It is her function to help the individual gain independence as rapidly as possible.

Each individual has the following needs which must be borne in mind when giving total (nursing) care:-

1. To breathe normally
2. To eat and drink adequately
3. To eliminate by all avenues of elimination
4. To move and maintain desirable posture
5. To sleep and rest
6. To select suitable clothing, dress and undress
7. To maintain normal body temperature by adjusting clothing and modifying environment
8. To keep body clean and well-groomed and protect the skin
9. To avoid dangers in the environment and avoid injuring others
10. To communicate with others in expressing emotions, needs and fears etc.
11. To worship according to his faith
12. To work at something that provides a sense of accomplishment
13. To play or participate in various forms of recreation
14. To learn, discover or satisfy the curiosity that leads to 'normal' development and health

(Virginia Henderson – "Principles of Basic Nursing Care").

1.   Skills

Some patients will require more help than others to fulfil these needs and special nursing skills are required in order to give this help. Those which should be learned in any ward experience are:-

The nurse should be able to-

Admit patients to hospital

Care for patients' clothing and personal belongings

Make patients comfortable in bed

Get patients out of bed

Bath patients in the bath

Prevent soreness of the skin

Keep patients' mouths clean

Care for patients' head and hair

Ensure that patients receive adequate nutrition

Attend to patients' sanitary needs

Take and record patients' temperature, pulse, respiration and weight

Measure and record fluid intake and output

Carry out routine urine tests

Prevent spread of infection

Communicate with patients, staff and visitors

Ensure that patients are kept suitably occupied

Observe and report on general condition and behaviour of patients

Maintain correct environment and prevent accidents

The special skills which can be learned in this ward are as follows:-

The nurse should be able to-

Care for a patient with: ileostomy, ileal loop, tracheostomy, gastrostomy, oesophagostomy
Care for a patient in an incubator or on a ventilator
Care for a patient receiving: intravenous fluids, intravenous alimentation

2.   Knowledge

The particular knowledge which should be acquired in this ward is as follows:-

a)   The nurse should be able to list the signs and symptoms, principles of treatment and care of the following conditions-

Circumcision	Duodenal Atresia
Undescended Testis	Ileal Atresia
Cystic Hygroma	Hirschsprung's Disease
Ectopic Bladder	Malrotation
Urinary Obstructions	Volvulus
*Urethral Valves	Exomphalos and Gastroschisis
Inguinal Hernia	Meconium Ileus
Umbilical Hernia	Imperforate Anus
Intussusception	Adhesions
Tracheo-oesophageal fistula	Prune Belly Baby
Oesophageal Atresia	Head Injury
Diaphragmatic Hernia	Subdural Effusion
Harelip, Cleft Palate	Neonatal Myelomeningocele & Hydrocephalus
*Urinary Abnormalities	Tumours

b) State actions, uses and side effects of the following drugs-

antibiotics   e.g. Gentamycin, Velosef
vitamins   e.g. Abidee
sedatives   e.g. Vallergan
analgesics
digoxin
frusimide

c) State reasons for the following investigations-

Gastro-intestinal tract: Barium swallow, meal, enema.
                         Oesophagoscopy
Respiratory tract: laryngoscopy, bronchogram
Urinary tract: Urinalysis, intravenous pyelogram,
                         cystogram, venogram

d) Observe and recognise the possible significance of the following
    complications-

bile stained vomiting
poor urine output
low or raised respiratory rate
low or raised pulse
low or raised blood pressure
abnormal breathing patterns
abnormal neurological observations
blocked valves
abdominal distension

e) Identify the nursing action to be taken and possible treatment when
    the above complications arise.

f)   State the role of other members of the hospital team for special care-

Physiotherapist
Dietitian
Bacteriologist
Pharmacist
Anaesthetist

g)   State the role of the Social Services available for the following patients-

spina bifida
cystic fibrosis
tracheostomy
colostomy
ileostomy
gastrostomy
oesophagostomy
poor housing conditions
unmarried parents
young parents

Senior nurses should be able to demonstrate their knowledge by teaching at report time and during teaching sessions.

3.   Attitudes

Attitudes which should be acquired in any ward are:-

The nurse will-

appreciate that each patient will have his own particular way of life which will affect his response to his stay in hospital

be willing to adapt as far as possible to the variations in needs of each individual

be aware of the importance of observation of patients

appreciate the importance of reporting observations and to act accordingly

appreciate the importance of maintaining a safe environment for patients and staff

appreciate the importance of establishing correct professional relationships with medical and paramedical staff and nursing colleagues

appreciate the role of the parents in cases of long term hospitalization and new-born abnormalities

appreciate the importance of economy and care of N.H.S. property.

In this ward, particular attitudes to be cultivated are:-

Awareness of the effect on the child of the following-

lack of food
lack of parental contact
lack of stimulation
tracheostomy
ripogle tube
restrictions from: intravenous therapy, restraints
incubator
ventilator

WAR YEARS

"Hope is grief's best music"

THE SECOND WORLD WAR 1939 – 1945

The Second World War caused death and destruction throughout the world. Queen Mary's Hospital for Children, like so many other hospitals and homes was hit by German bombs and rockets, in wave after wave of attacks by enemy aircraft and V1 and V2 rockets.

Queen Mary's was the most heavily bombed hospital in London. Various reasons have been given for this: its close proximity to Croydon Airport, its aerial appearance being similar to the layout of army barracks, and the fact that German bombers discharged their surplus bombs before flying back over the Channel after attacking London. The first bombing of the hospital occurred in 1940.

Eventually, with the new threats posed by the V1 and V2 rockets, total evacuation of the hospital was decided upon on July 21st 1944 and the children taken by coach and train to a number of locations in England and Wales. The school was split between Dryburn Emergency

Hospital at Durham and Scotton Banks Hospital, Knaresborough, Yorkshire.

After VE Day 1945, the premises were re-occupied, but the war damage meant that the beds were reduced from 1,284 to 840.

Patients out on the Ward Veranda

Photograph taken on the day that the British Prime Minister, Neville Chamberlain, and the Western Allies declared war on Germany, September 3rd 1939, following the attack on Poland on September 1st.

Kindly contributed by Mr W A Neil at my exhibition and book signing at the Sutton Heritage Centre.

The following photographs of the Second World War
and Post War years were kindly contributed by:
Miss J F Howell, Staff Nurse Rita Grassi (nee Kiewe), the County
Durham Health Authority, the Pathology Laboratory at the New
Dryburn Hospital and Nurse Pauline Richmond.

Nurse Rita Kiewe with
baby on D8 - 1943

Nurse Rita Kiewe outside
Chapel - Oct. 1943

1943

Rita Kiewe - Staff Nurse
25-7-1947

*Evacuation from Queen Mary's Hospital to Scotton Banks
Hospital, Knaresborough on the hospital train 1944*

At Scotton Banks Hospital,
Knaresborough 1944

131

Above: *Rita Kiewe with four friends*
                 taken at Scotton Banks
                 Hospital when evacuated in
                 1944
Top right: Nurses Rita Kiewe, Hilda
                 Khan, Marjorie Norman and
                 Beattie Boyd at Scotton
                 Banks May 26th 1945
Right: *Staff Nurse Rita Kiewe with*
                 two patients at Queen
                 Mary's, Ward D8 1947
Below: *At Queen Mary's in 1947*

132

Matron, Deputy Matron and Nurses at a Tea Dance. Queen Mary's - 4th December 1945

Outside the main administration building

Devastation of a ward

A boarded up ward

Digging for Victory

Fete Day? Men in military uniform - date uncertain

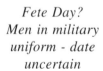

QUEEN MARY'S
MOST FREQUENTLY BOMBED OF ALL LCC
AND MDB HOSPITALS AROUND LONDON

Places bombed that surrounded Queen Mary's
Croydon Airport
Denmark Road
Anglesey Gardens
Dalmeny Road
Acre Lane
Rothfield Road
Kings Arms Pub Carshalton High Street
behind Windsor Castle
between Salisbury Road, War Memorial Hospital
Erskine Road
Fellows Road
29 Acres
Love Lane
Lavender Road
Farm Lane
Gordon Road

Flying Bombs
Stanley Park Road
Staplehurst Road
Burleigh Avenue
Wallington Garden Green
Ceders Road, Sutton
West Way

V.2.
Just off Boundary Road in to Banstead Asylum (on open ground).

Contributed by John Vinn (91 years of age)
Demolition and Rescue Parties Supervisor for Bombs

NEWSPAPER REPORT 12th October 1944

Over a period of time, 27 V1 Flying bombs fell in Carshalton, killing 25 people. 165 homes were totally destroyed.

Rest centres for bombed-out victims were established at Westwenth Hall, Methodist Central Hall, Green Wrythe Lane, Bishopsford Hall and Poulter Park.

The V1s started landing in the middle of June 1944 and the months of June and July saw frequent attacks. Hence the decision to completely evacuate Queen Mary's.

THE EVACUATION TO DURHAM
JULY 25TH 1944

The following reports appeared in the Durham Advertiser on August 11th 1944. Shortly after, approximately 200 of the Queen Mary's children were evacuated to Durham. I can only assume that the sickly children referred to here came from Queen Mary's.

These articles have been reproduced by kind permission of Mr Peter Barron, Editor of the Northern Echo.

Emergency Rest Centre

The emergency rest centre was prepared and conducted for the Durham County Public Assistance Committee by Mr A S Smith (relieving officer), with the help of his colleague, Mr Brains, and a large number of voluntary helpers. These included Mr W N Illingworth (officer-in-charge), Mrs Hudson (leader of the women personnel), Miss Viola Fleming, teachers and the caretaker of the City Senior School, Miss Ryans and members of the staff of the school canteen, ladies resident in and near Whinney Hill, a number of boy scouts and boys and girls of the City Senior School. In its co-operation with the City Council, the rest centre had the help of Miss Holliday in the provision of meals. The rest centre organisation was responsible for the domestic arrangements, such as those for meals and sleeping, washing, recreation and 'the personal touch'. In looking after the babies and the sickly and slightly injured evacuees, and in assisting the medical examinations, the rest centre had the help of Nurse Tredennick, Nurse Spence, Mrs Barrett and her staff, Nurse Sakell, Nurse Holmes, Miss Bradley, Mrs

Uzzel and Mrs Davies.[1] Air raid wardens, under the superintendence of Mr George Greenwell (chief warden), dealt with the luggage of the evacuees, and some wardens remained all night.

Some of the mothers asked whether they were in Scotland or on the Border, and seemed astonished to hear that another county came before Scotland. On hearing that they were only ten miles from the East Coast their faces fell, for 'the East Coast' to them meant a danger zone. They were taken to the school geography room and shown a map.[2] They had heard of Wales as a safe place for evacuation, but on seeing that Durham was further from London than even Wales they declared, "Well, the Government knew what they were doing when they sent us here!" One of the escorts who accompanied the evacuees said, "You people of the North have a reputation for giving a kind and hearty welcome, and you have lived up to it today."

Mayor's Welcome

As soon as the train pulled into the station, the Mayor (Councillor W A H Shepherd) extended welcome, and hoped the evacuees would have a very happy time even if their stay in the city would be brief. He was accompanied by Mr G R Bull, Town Clerk, Mr C A Vessey, deputy Town Clerk, Mr A E Jones, billeting officer, and officials of the County P.A.C., under Mr Whitfield-Jackson, who acted in place of Mr R B Hindmarch, unavoidably absent. Members of the W.V.S. Civil Defence and many others gave every assistance.

Altogether the Southerners numbered 394, of whom 58 were mothers, 75 children under five years, 85 over five years and 176 unaccompanied children.

By kindness of the Council of Durham Colleges, 115 beds were provided at the University, St Mary's and Hatfield Colleges.

In an interview, the Town Clerk said as a result of a survey there would seem at the moment a lack of voluntary billets for certain evacuees, but it was to be hoped when actual billeting began the public would come forward voluntarily to make up the deficiency. If sufficient numbers of voluntary billets were not forthcoming there would be no alternative to using a compulsion.

Constables under Supt. T Hetherington, Inspectors H Alcock and W Nixon were marshals and controlled traffic in and around the station and school.

More evacuees expected

We are informed by the Town Clerk (Mr George R Bull) that the 394 evacuees recently received in the city have been accommodated. He has been informed that a further batch of 400 may be expected, and desires it to be known that unless a large number of voluntary billets is forthcoming there will be no option but to resort to compulsory measures.

1. Queen Mary's is presumably not mentioned specifically due to wartime reporting censorship.
2. The Butler Education Act of 1944 introduced the Tripartite system of free secondary education for all, based on ability and not on parental income. All children could now be educated at a Grammar, Secondary Modern or Technical School according to age, aptitude or ability.

Jean from Durham 14.4.97

I remember the Hospital being built as I came to Durham in 1941. Queen Mary's would have been the first in Dryburn as you know it was an Emergency Military Hospital, I plainly remember the wounded soldiers walking around in blue suits. There was also a ward for German prisoners of war, when my sisters and me were invited to Queen Mary's Christmas party we passed the ward were the Germans were and we could hear them singing (carols) we stopped to listen but were told to move on. There was a Nurse English of Queen Mary's she tap danced at the party and her soldier boy friend was also there. There was a boy patient by the name of Sydney Spears. When Dryburn was built I don't think there would be any more than eight to ten wards it is now our main Hospital very big. I have tried very hard to get information of first years of Dryburn without success apart from my sisters and me no one knows any thing about Dryburn's beginning at Queen Mary's as I've said to you before with it being a Military Hospital in wartime it was hush hush. If I do get any more news (as I'm still searching) I shall let you have it.

DRYBURN – PAST AND PRESENT

The 'centre' of Dryburn Hospital is Dryburn Hall. This is an interesting small mansion house and was built in 1824 as the Seat of William Lloyd Wharton. The Wharton family had been associated with Durham since the 17th century and had played active roles in civic life. The founding of Durham Regatta and of Wharton Park were both due to the benevolence of the founder of this mansion.

There is in existence an 18th century document which describes 'The Land Preview'. In this document we read: "Under Hatfield's survey, John de Baumbrough held a messuage and sixty one acres and a half, once Robert Leycester's called Dryburn-house, by Knight's service and 41s.2d. rent. In 1595, Richard Hutchinson purchased the tenement, called Drawdon from Mathew Farales. In 1607, Christopher Hutchinson, son and heir of Richard, conveyed to Oswald and Mary Baker. In 1610, Mary and her second husband, William Smith, Esq., granted Drawden or Dryburn to Nicholas Hutchinson, who settled this estate on his second son, Cuthbert, in 1622. Cuthbert Hutchinson (son of Cuthbert) sold

Dryburn Emergency Military Hospital opened in 1942
(Photo courtesy of Pathology Laboratory, Dryburn Hospital)

Dryburn to his relative John Hutchinson, Esq., of Framwellgate, whose great grandson John Hutchinson, Esq., held this property in 1760. It was soon after purchased by the family of Wharton and is now the estate of Mrs Wharton, widow of the Rev. Robert Wharton, Chancellor of Lincoln."

There was probably a hospital on or near this site in the past. There is reference to a "Spittle House hard by Drawdon, or Dryburn".

The present hospital at Dryburn began its life in 1942 when it was opened as an emergency military hospital. It had been developed on a site owned by Durham County Council, part of which had been earmarked before the war to build a general hospital of 340 beds. The hospital was built with the intention of accommodating 800 military personnel. After the war, civilian patients were treated in the hospital.

At the inception of the NHS, the Regional Hospital Board decided to start upgrading Dryburn Hospital to ensure that the community received the best service possible. This upgrading and service improvement still continues. The following have been among the larger projects and service improvements over the past 40 years:

- The X-Ray Department was soon inadequate to meet the needs of the catchment area, so a new Department was built in 1954. Further improvements have continued through the years.

- In 1962 the Nuffield Ward was built to accommodate patients who were almost ready for discharge from hospital. This building, no longer used as a ward, now houses the Medical Physics Department and the Occupational Health Department – both giving vital services to the district.

- Throughout the country, hospitals were going over to have equipment sterilised centrally and in 1964 the CSSD Department at Dryburn was built. The same year, the Triple Theatre suite was opened. Theatres had previously been housed in what is now the I.T.U. Department. To improve the Maternity and Paediatric Services, Ward 9 and the Special Care Baby Unit were opened in 1964.

- The need for more housing for Pathology services was next considered and in 1969 the Pathology Department was extended into a new building.

- Also in 1969, the Postgraduate Medical Centre was opened. This building had previously been the Nurse Training School, which was now transferred to the Nurse Residence at North End.

- In 1970 what had been the Operating Theatre, X-Ray and some Pathology laboratories were converted into the present I.T.U.

- The Orthopaedic Wards and the Accident and Emergency Department opened in 1971 when the services were transferred from the County Hospital which was no longer considered appropriate for the treatment and nursing of surgical patients.

- The spiritual care of patients was not forgotten and the hospital chapel, paid for by the Friends, was opened in 1972.

- For some time it had been considered necessary to have a purpose built ward for care of the Young Disabled and, with this in mind Dunelm Ward was built. It has 20 beds for young disabled patients and those suffering from neurological diseases.

- Over the years the number of Outpatient appointments increased annually and more accommodation was needed, so in 1976 the Outpatient Department 'B' was opened. This purpose-built building houses clinics for Paediatric, Geriatric, Ophthalmic and ENT patients.

- More recently a new Medical Records Storage facility was needed and when this was built the first floor became Ward 18 – a Ward of 25 beds for both sexes. This was opened in 1982.

- In 1983 storage space was needed for the CSSD and a new store was opened at the back of the Theatre Suite. The CSSD now serves five Theatres, all the Wards and the Community Services.

- Also in 1983 a new Maternity Classroom was built to house 18 students for the Midwifery Training School.

It seems that almost every year some upgrading has taken place within Dryburn. The latest development soon to be commissioned is a further extension to the Pathology Laboratory to enable the provision from Dryburn of a Cervical Cytology service.

In spite of all this building and upgrading, however, Dryburn is still congested and some departments are not as close to others as they ought to be. The younger staff all look forward to the future and to the start of the new District General Hospital. Let us hope that day is not too far off.

We should remember, however, that a hospital is its staff. All disciplines work together for the good of the patient and the community.

Mr K Lawrence-Edward
Senior Nurse, Dryburn

Mr Kevin Keegan at the present Dryburn Children's Unit
kindly contributed by former Queen Mary's Staff Nurse Pauline Richmond

PULSE

THE HOSPITAL WARDS

We have wondered whether or not to give the ages of our contributors after their names. The difficulty here is that many children in Queen Mary's have had such severe educational handicaps that ages often lose their significance. However, we have given the ward numbers where relevant and for the interest of readers we give in this issue a list of wards with the type of each.

A1	Acute Surgical
A2	Acute Surgical and Orthopaedic
B1	Acute Medical
B2	Acute Medical
B3	Acute Medical
C7	Orthopaedic
C8	Unit for Emotionally disturbed children
D1	Orthopaedic
D7	Rehabilitation
D8	Myelemeningocoele
E2	Acute Medical
E9	Muscular Dystrophy
E10	Muscular Dystrophy
F3	Long Stay Medical
F8	Cerebral Palsy Unit

Also Autistic Unit: drawn from several wards.

The children's magazine Pulse was first published in the autumn of 1963. Extracts from Pulse are printed here, starting with the article 'Another Star on E10' published on the 2nd December 1963. Pulse was produced by the boys on E10 and originally cost 3 old pence. From its first editions it rapidly became a very polished and professional magazine. One of its contributors, Stuart Oliver, was later to become a journalist with 'Sporting Life'. His article on the Grand National 1965 is also reproduced from The Pulse No. 8 starting on p154.

THE PULSE NO.2 DECEMBER 1963

Another Star on E10

Mr Pastry, well known TV star, came to Queen Mary's to present £1,000 for a swimming pool to be built in the hospital. After he made his way round to some of the wards, one of these being E10. He was wearing one of Matron's caps and he signed autographs.

THE PULSE NO.3 MARCH 1964

Queen Mary's Youth Club

About a year ago, some boys from different wards had occasionally thought how nice it would be if they could meet regularly. With the help of Mr Joseph (of 'The Friends of Queen Mary's) the idea of a Youth Club was put forward and a provisional committee met to consider it.

Mr Joseph brought to the meeting Mr Jim Sharman who was chosen as leader. Mr Graham True, who was not there on that occasion, was chosen as his deputy. Joint Treasurers (Taffy Thomas and Tommy Fletcher) were elected from Ward E10 and Peter Woods and I took on the secretarial duties. Thirteen was fixed as the lower age limit for membership.

Since then we have had meetings every Thursday from 6.30 to 8.30 in the Recreation Hall. Some weeks we have had a 'Beat' group for the second hour and sometimes 'Bingo'.

We have a little Coffee Bar; hot drinks are supplied by the hospital and soft drinks and other items can be purchased over the counter.

Apart from the games we have together, some like to play chess, draughts or cards, or just talk while listening to records.

We have helpers, some from other Youth Clubs, and others from schools round about.

by John Sandell (Hon. Secretary)

THE PULSE NO.4 MAY 1964

Matron's visit to Sweden

We have pleasure in giving you Matron's account of her visit to Sweden.

"In October, 1963, I went to Sweden to visit Hospitals, Health Centres and Residential Schools. I travelled by train from London to Tilbury, where I joined a Swedish ship, SS 'Souecia'. This is a very nice ship which carries 450 passengers. The North Sea was very calm and smooth and after a most pleasant crossing, which takes about 42 hours, I arrived in Gothenburg which is a very old city. I then travelled by train to Stockholm. The Swedish trains are very modern and fast, and the scenery on this journey is quite magnificent.

Stockholm is a very interesting city and, as you probably know, is called 'The Venice of the North'. It is, of course, much smaller than London but the traffic is quite frightening. Although cars are driven on the left hand side of the road as in England, they are almost all 'left-hand drive'. The taxis are all Mercedes – very comfortable and luxurious and, of course, expensive. I saw a notice outside a Theatre in Stockholm announcing the forthcoming visit of the Beatles the following week and I must let you into a secret – at that time I had not heard of them.

I also visited Uppsala which is another University Town, but very old. The Catherdral is most interesting.

The Swedish people are very friendly and hospitable. Almost everyone speaks English which is the second language in Sweden since the last war.

The children start school at the age of 7 and English lessons begin during their fourth year at school. The children speak English with an American accent.

Sweden is a very nice clean country but everything is very expensive. I enjoyed visiting the various hospitals but, I must say, I was very pleased to get back to Queen Mary's.

I came home on the SS 'Britannia', a sister ship of the 'Souecia'. These two ships pass each other in the North Sea on every voyage, and we went on deck to see the 'Souecia'. There was much waving and cheering while both ships' sirens hooted.

I hope you will enjoy reading this very brief account of my visit to Sweden."

Loose Change

Have you ever wondered how our coinage came into being? How we adopted the penny, sixpence, shilling, and so on? It has a long and interesting history.

The crown of five shilling piece for instance was, until comparatively recently a standard coin, the largest silver coin and almost universal, the words Crown, Kroner, Daler or Dollar are almost synonymous.

The first appeared in the reign of Henry VIII. It was originally a small gold coin, but with the spending habits of this King, gold was scarce and it was issued first in silver and then in alloy with a thin covering of silver. The extent of the debasing was so great that the silver wore off on parts of the coins and result was that Henry VIII was nicknamed 'Old Copper nose' from the effect on his prominent feature on the alloy crowns.

After Henry's death, the economists tried to counteract the effect of his extravagance and their first task was to establish a stable coinage. They issued, among other coins, a large silver crown with a value of 5/ - and so our modern crown was born. The first crown is extremely rare and a beautiful example of the art of minting. It shows the King mounted on a horse (Edward I as a child), and the reverse showed the Royal Coat of Arms. The next issue was in the reign of Elizabeth I. The coin shows her in the magnificence of her robes wearing her crown and holding the sceptre.

In Elizabeth's reign, the first English piece of eight was minted for merchants to use abroad. As we were at war, it was hoped that the 'Portcullis Dollar' as it became known, would be accepted as a basis for foreign trade. It was mistrusted, however, and fell out of use very quickly.

England's first and only dictator issued a crown piece, it has the inscription 'The Commonwealth of England' and showed the Cross of St George and the Harp of Ireland.

Since that date there have been a succession of crowns issued, the last being in 1960. Some are magnificent specimens of minting as the size of the coin gives room for good design ... More about coins in the next issue.

146

THE PULSE NO. 5 SEPT 1964

A visit from British athletes

In June we had a visit at the Youth Club from four athletes, showing us a film of a recent tour of Russia by the British Athletics team. The athletes were Ann Packer, Joy Jordon, Mike Fleet and the British Olympic Team Captain – Robbie Brightwell, and we asked him to give us his autograph, which we have printed below.

Robbie Brightwell is one of the best quarter milers in the world, and should have a good chance of winning a gold medal for Britain in Tokyo.

by Thomas Fletcher

Loose Change

DID YOU KNOW?

The current shillings in Scotland are different – they show the Idon of Scotland rampant on the reverse instead of the three lions of England (couchant).

A gold 70 ducat piece of Poland, dated 1621, was sold in London last month for £3,000. This coin is the largest gold coin in the world, being two and three quarter inches across and weighing over half a pound.

A new half dollar coin was issued in the United States in February 1964. It shows the portrait of President Kennedy although he died in 1963.

The shilling of George I issued in 1720 has the following inscription (in Latin) – "George I by the Grace of God of Great Britain, France and Ireland, King, Defender of the Faith, Duke of Brunswick and Luneberg, Arch Treasurer and Elector of the Holy Roman Empire".

The first gold coins to be issued in the world at face value since devaluation in 1931 were placed on sale in April 1963. The country? – Tonga, formerly the Friendly Isles in the South West Pacific. Values 1 Koula, ½ Koula and ¼ Koula (1 Koula is equivalent to £16 sterling).

A 1951 penny in mint condition fetches about £2.10s.0d.

A gold Charles II crown piece was sold at auction in London this month for £1,281.

A designer usually has his initials on coins. They are clearly visible on George VI half-crowns at the base of the neck – H.P. (Harry Paget).

Those humble coins, farthings, are enjoying a vogue in the United States. Some of the earlier issues are being eagerly purchased at 1/- each upwards!!

The smallest English coin is the silver two-penny piece which ceased issue in Victorian times (except in Maundy money).

Maundy money is a gift from the Sovereign to poor persons and this custom dates back to medieval times. It is so called because the gifts are distributed on Maundy Thursday and in recent times consisted of a set of specially minted coins in a purse. The sets are in great demand by collectors and the recipients of the gifts can sell them for a considerable sum if they wish.

9d. stands for nine pence. Why 'd' and not 'p'? 'd' is an abbreviation for denarius, an ancient Roman coin.

THE PULSE NO. 6 NOV 1964

Paris 1964

The chance of a life time came to another dozen of our children this year, as three girls and nine boys left Queen Mary's Hospital at 8.15 am on a lovely summer morning, bound for Paris. The journey was in three stages – coach to Newhaven – then by boat to Dieppe, and a long ride in a new coach to Garche, near Paris. An unexpected sea mist in mid Channel was the only problem encountered on the outward journey.

The weather was wonderful during the eight days holiday, though at times it was too hot. Some of us were able to cool down in the hospital swimming pool, and a few were able to enjoy open-air swimming during the week.

As "S.S. Brighton" (our ship) drew near the landing stage at Dieppe, friends were already waving a welcome to Mr Joseph and other members of the party. Soon we were off the boat and on the quay – France at last – being greeted with French cordiality by Mademoiselle Jacqueline and her friend Mademoiselle Gelly. After some light refreshments in a nearby cafe, we boarded a large and luxurious coach bound for Paris – about 150 miles distant, and enjoyed the ride. We arrived at the Raymond Poincare Hospital tired but cheerful. Friends were there to greet us with many words we could not understand and many smiles that we could. They gave us a lovely meal, the first of many more that we were to enjoy during our stay, then away we went to find our sleeping quarters and settle down for our first night in France.

The experiences of the following days are pleasant memories but some events stand out very clearly. Such was the visit to the Eiffel Tower. There we spent nearly two hours surveying Paris from the first platform. How lovely it looked in every direction with the Seine wandering its way through the city. How the Seine loves Paris!

Our friend Simon was 13 years old on that day, so we presented him with a little model of the Eiffel Tower to commemorate the occasion. We descended the Tower by lift except for two adult helpers who, for a dare, walked down the winding stairs. They arrived at ground level almost at the same time as the rest. Then we drove back to Garches via the Louvre Palace, the Tuileries, Champs E'lysées, the Arc de Triomphe and the lovely Bois de Bologne gardens.

We shall never forget the long trip by coach nearly 100 miles south, to the Loire Valley. It was a hot but interesting ride so we were glad of the shade of some trees at Sully, where we spent some time near the castle. Eight members of the party had a cool bathe in the River Loire. Lucky things!

One afternoon was spent visiting two famous areas of Paris – the Sacre Coeur, (with the artists' paradise behind it), and the Notre Dame Cathedral. Then, after resting in the gardens behind the Cathedral, we had another sightseeing tour of the area around the 'Island City' before going to the Solverino Restaurant for an unforgettable dinner. From here we drove to the river and boarded a large motor boat for a night trip on the Seine. The atmosphere of Paris by night is even more romantic when gliding under sixteen bridges, past famous places described by a young and pretty Parisienne, whose English was broken but certainly pleasant.

No visit to Paris is complete without going to Versailles. This we did twice, first to drive round the grand canal and visit the village of Marie Antoinette; later to visit the famous Palace and its fabulous treasures. We shall ever remember the complex clock of Louis XIV which was set in motion specially for our benefit by the Curator. "Your Versailles," said the guide who showed us round and made everything so interesting.

One trip 30 miles north of Paris was made even more enjoyable by the biggest picnic meal imaginable. We wondered when these kindly French would stop unloading exotic eatables!, and how anyone could eat all those items in one meal – meat, eggs, ham, cheese, lettuce, tomato, fruit, biscuits, roll, butter ... !! However, the lovely woodland glade seemed to sharpen our appetites and all did valiantly, further encouraged by cool soft drinks brought in an ice box.

So the days flashed by with further visits to Orly Airport, Chantilly Racecourses, and the Pasteur Institute. Food, friendship, and fine weather – all in good quantity – made "Paris 1964" memorable. Of these three, surely we regard the middle one of supreme value. We thank all friends on both sides of the Channel who contributed to the great success of the holiday, in particular the ladies who fed us, the drivers who tirelessly catered for our journeying needs, and Mlle. Jacqueline, our constant guide and companion during our stay. Au revoir – merci, merci beaucoup.

by G. Hadfield

THE PULSE NO. 7 MARCH 1965

Donations to Queen Mary's
In 1959 the then Minister of Health decided that the Fountain and the Carshalton Hospital Management Committees should amalgamate in order to develop at Queen Mary's Hospital for Children, a comprehensive hospital caring in the one hospital for both physically and mentally handicapped children. This was a new pioneering concept.

In the five years since then, many voluntary bodies and private people have shown their support of this new venture by donating not only large but also many small sums towards some of the hospital's objectives.

Jewish Aid Committee
The Jewish Aid Committee for Mentally Handicapped Children has been a wholehearted supporter of the comprehensive hospital. They decided in 1959 to award £100 a year for 10 years for the Hospital Management Committee to give to the nurse who each

year was judged the one who had made the best contribution towards the comprehensive concept. Four members of the nursing staff have so far won this prize, and three of them have been abroad as a result of it, to study hospitals in foreign countries. This year Sister Agnes West of Ward F5 went to Germany and last year the Matron, Miss Jones, went to Sweden.

The Jewish Aid Committee has also raised nearly £6,000 which, together with a donation of £4,500 from the King Edward's Hospital Fund for London, will build in the grounds of the hospital a block of four flatlets. Each flatlet will have a double bed-sitting room, a single room, a kitchenette and a bathroom. The idea of this is that parents may spend a weekend or even longer in the flatlets with their child who is normally in a ward.

Swimming Pool

Mr Richard Hearne, know to TV fans as Mr Pastry, decided to launch an appeal for funds for a swimming pool for the hospital. Although he put himself at the head of the appeal he needed a local voluntary committee to undertake much hard work and organisation. Three local Round Table clubs provided members, together with representatives from the Barrow Hedges Parent-Teacher Association. Mr Hearne and this committee, supported by the Hospital's League of Friends and senior Officers, have so far raised over £7,000 towards a total cost which will be in the region of £10,000. The pool will be enclosed and so usable all the year round and will be in two parts – a large area for paddling and a small area for swimming.

Variety Club

The League of Friends and the Variety Club of Great Britain have very generously donated three coaches – one from the League and two from the Variety Club – each costing approximately £3,000. Most patients will have experienced rides, long and short, in these purpose built vehicles for handicapped children.

Sports Pavilion

Most patients, too, will have seen the excellent Sports Pavilion which was completed about a year ago near the cricket pitch. This cost about £12,000 and the money was provided by the King

Edward's Hospital Fund and the Regional Hospital Board – the latter from its endowment funds.

League of Friends
The League of Friends has, of course, been exceptionally generous in many ways, but two most recent gifts are the Pet's Corner, or Zoo, towards which they provided £1,500 plus a sum of £100 for new animals; and nearly £4,000 to provide, at the main entrance to the hospital, a canteen and centre for the League and for parents visiting the hospital. There will also be facilities for the Hospital's Youth Club to meet there if they so desire.

£10,000 a year
The recent announcement by the Drapers' Company who have promised to provide £10,000 each year for five years, is a great excitement and will, it is hoped, enable the Management Committee to build a school for mentally and physically handicapped children, more modern than the existing one and nearer to the centre of the hospital.

£20,000 will
The will of the late Miss Drew has not yet been proved but the solicitors have shown that there is approximately £20,000, much of which will come to the hospital in due course. The Committee have not yet decided how this money will be spent because, due to certain legal clauses, it may be several years before we receive it.

In addition to these sums, we have received other amounts in the region of from £1,000 to £3,000 from research laboratories and from the Variety Club and the National Society for Mentally Handicapped Children in order to pay for essential research into certain specialities which are connected with this hospital.

Support
The interest which is being taken by many people in the district in this hospital is shown from the result of the appeal for the Swimming Pool. Many small sums of approximately £1 - £5 are received from both individuals and organisations, but some organisations such as the Cheam (St Andrews) Scout Group and

the Selsdon (Afternoon) Townswomen's Guild, send sums of £50 or more.

All this support shows that many organisations and people in a wide area around the hospital are keenly interested in its welfare and are prepared to assist it in every possible way in order to make it a complete success.

by K. G. Perona-Wright FCIS, FHA

PETS CORNER - An Open Letter to All the Children

Dear Boys and Girls

When I first arrived at Queen Mary's I was told that one of my very varied duties would be that of Head Zoo Keeper. Thinking of the antics of my own children, I merely laughed and said that I had plenty of experience already – the laugh became somewhat weak when I found that the Pets Corner really existed. However, as a small boy, I was reared on a farm where, in addition to a pony, I was always looking after small lambs, piglets, calves and a variety of wild birds, from Peregrine Falcons to tame jackdaws, so I was not too daunted by the prospect before me.

When choosing the inhabitants for the Pets Corner, I had to think about the accommodation available for them, the amount of care they need and also about the purpose of a Pets Corner in a hospital. This is, first, to help children to overcome some of their natural fears of animals and birds, second to become a centre of interest for them during their walks around the grounds and third, to be a central point where brothers and sisters can stay whilst parents are visiting in the wards.

With all this in mind, we set out to provide colour and movement with animals and birds which are easy to look after and which are quite hardy in our English climate. Our first acquisitions were some guinea-pigs (or cavies) and two rabbits. These have all settled down well together (with various family additions), and make a pleasant picture, basking in patches of sunlight, or playing games of 'tag', as the younger rabbits do from time to time. For the main aviary, we have been given some very colourful budgerigars who, if they are not flying around, are always chattering away quite happily. In here too, we have two 'Spreole Starlings' with red-brown chests and shiny blue wings and backs – their colouring is lovely and from time to time they sing very prettily indeed.

The other inmates of the aviary are various types of tanagers – blue, silver winged and yellow rumped, who add lovely splashes of colour and have settled in happily enough, despite their plaintive call. To complete the colony in the aviary, we hope soon to collect some Red Cardinals and some Peking Robins, both very colourful and attractive species.

Next to the aviary, we have the cage which now houses four young Malabar Squirrels. These squirrels will grow to about twice their present size. They came originally from India, and are the kind from which Walt Disney developed his own squirrel friends in so many films. The end cage is occupied by three cock golden pheasants, a family of four bantams crossed with Malayan Jungle Fowl, and, at the moment, Marlene, our Pea-Hen. George, the Peacock, is allowed out already, and we hope that by early spring next year he will know his way around sufficiently well so that Marlene can come out to join him.

That completes our little trip around Pets Corner, but I hope that you will come to see the birds and animals as often as you can, and that you will enjoy your visits. Please try, though, not to feed the birds and animals – they all have carefully controlled diets which contain all that is best for them and all that they need.

(Reprinted from The Fountain Magazine, for which acknowledgement and grateful thanks are sent to the Editorial Committee by the Editor.)

by J. J-P. Atwill

THE PULSE NO. 8 JUNE 1965

The Last Post or Freddie just 'Trumped'

Out on a warm sunlit afternoon on March 27th, 1965, the American twosome – Tommy Smith and Jay Trump – won the 126 renewal, and possibly last Grand National by a hard-fought three-quarters of a length, from Scottish trained Freddie. But all that is history now, and so are the other 125 Grand Nationals.

It was on Saturday, February 25th 1839, at Aintree, Liverpool, that an aptly named horse, Lottery, ploughed his way through four and a half miles and jumped thirty of the roughest, toughest obstacles in the world to win the first Grand National.

Since that far off cold, bleak Saturday afternoon, the Grand National has become the world's greatest steeplechase and it has modelled itself into an event of great tradition and history.

It came as a staggering shock when it was announced on Wednesday, July 1st, last year, that the course is to close down for housing development. Homes for the homeless are important, but in the bottom of my heart, I honestly and truly believe that the Grand National is too.

A Grand National held anywhere else would be the same in name only.

No other racecourses in the world could stage the Grand National as we know it. No other course could build the Aintree fences consisting of thirty tons of gorse to build one fence. Each fence takes six weeks to complete, and even if they could rebuild the fences, they can never remove tradition. Whoever tries, it can only be a pale, bloodless shadow of the real thing.

What is it, do you suppose, that fires the hearts and fills the dreams of those who ride, train, own, or merely watch horses running in the world's greatest steeplechase?

It is, of course, the past – the century and a quarter throughout which men and horses have struggled, suffered and sometimes died on this same misty, barren windswept stretch of ground. Just to ride in the race, however slender their chances, the jockeys realise that they have written a tiny line in Aintree's many chapters.

The brook the huge field thundered over last March was the self same brook where Captain Martin Becher (Becher's Brook) and his mount Conrad, hit the dust in the inaugural Grand National. The Canal Turn is the same fence across which East Hero lay helpless in 1929 to bring thirty horses crashing to the ground, and the run in is that same long staring street of grass on which the Queen Mother's Devon Loch collapsed with the race at his mercy, fifty yards from the winning post in 1956. To Devon Loch's jockey, Dick Francis, it must have seemed like a heavenly dream – a dream that turned to a nightmare seconds before the dawn.

It is these and a thousand other memories which make the Grand National – and they can never be transplanted. Aintree is their home and only at Aintree (speaking from a jockey's point of view) can one feel the almost unbearable mixture of hope and fear that grips their hearts and minds as the field lines up on National day. Each hopes that he is about to fulfil a lifelong ambition, which originated as a schoolboy dream as he sat gazing at the ceiling and chewing his pencil, and that is to win the most gruelling of all steeplechases. Each also knows that it is highly probable that in just over nine minutes time, one of them, whether it be man or beast, will never be the same again. One of the noble creatures may have seen his stable for the last time, each rider wonders if he has seen his home for the last time. It is not easy to forget that in the past 126 years only 478 of the 1,047 competitors have completed the course.

If all this sounds sentimental, too dramatic, I make no apology. The Grand National is dramatic. I am sentimental about it and have been ever since I drew Royal Tan in a school sweepstake eleven years ago and listened, wondering, with little or no idea what it was all about, as Brian Marshall drove him home.

It was to be a long arduous road for me before I took the great interest in racing I do today.

I have written this article to given the layman some idea what the Grand National means to Britain and to prove that the Grand National is not just a race which all betting fanatics can squander the rent money and/or family allowance on. The Grand National is a piece of British history. It has been respected and admired by the British and their sovereigns throughout the ages. The Grand National is something Britain gave the world. Something for which the world should be grateful, and of which all Englishmen have reason to be proud. Should it close then a link with the past will die. There is fresh hope that the course may be saved. Tophams, the current owners of the course, have been restrained from selling the course by its former owner Lord Sefton in his life time. At the moment all the principals are fighting for the survival of Aintree.

So let them fight to the last ditch to rescue Aintree – and only when that battle is lost, start to pick up and put together the pieces of a shattered dream.

Stuart Oliver

THE PULSE NO. 9 NOV 1965

Group Secretary's Report

Jewish Aid Committee

You will remember from the last article that the Jewish Aid Committee and King Edward's Hospital Fund were providing the necessary money to build four flatlets. These are almost completed – there are just one or two items to be finished, but then the committee still have a problem with regard to the expense of furnishing these flatlets, but it is hoped that one or two of them will be ready by Christmas.

Swimming Pool

The Swimming Pool also is almost completed. There are just one or two final details outstanding but it is hoped it will be ready within the next two or three weeks.

As the pool is heated we shall be able to start using it immediately. It has, however, provisionally been arranged that the official opening will take place on 19th December when Mr Pastry will also tour the hospital with Father Christmas.

League of Friends

The Friends' Centre, built at the cost of some £4,000 was recently opened by the Chairman, Lord Grenfell. In future this Centre will be used on Sundays by parents visiting the hospital. It will be possible to buy tea, ice cream, chocolates etc., in the Centre, instead of in the Recreation Hall. In due course, the League of Friends will also give consideration to the Centre being used for other purposes. It is, for example, hoped that perhaps the Committee of the Youth Club will be able to hold its meetings in the Friends' Centre and we are also exploring other ways in which the Centre could be used during the week for hospital and social purposes.

Drapers' Company School

The Drapers' Company School is still being considered and another meeting of the project team which is designing the School will take place in the hospital within the next two or three weeks, when it is hoped that we shall be able to complete the plans. Even after the plans are drawn up it will be a year or so before we have enough money to be able to start building this project.

Sir Winston Churchill's bust

A bust of Sir Winston Churchill was recently sculptured by a member of the staff, Mr J Cao Lata, who is a Spaniard working in the hospital as a Ward Orderly. He presented the bust to the hospital and this will be placed in the entrance to the Nurses' Home in the fairly near future.

French Visit

The French Authorities from the Hospital in France who exchange patients with us on an annual basis have written to say how delighted they were with all the arrangements that were made. They were particularly grateful to the patients and staff who entertained the French children in the Recreation Hall on two occasions. They have asked that their thanks should be given to all involved in this.

by K G Perona-Wright

THE PULSE NO. 11 JULY 1966

Our New Swimming Pool

Princess Marina, Duchess of Kent, officially opened the 'Mr Pastry' Swimming Pool here at Queen Mary's Hospital, on Saturday, 5th February 1966.

This was the first visit of a member of the Royal Family since Queen Mary named the hospital in 1914.

The Princess arrived at the hospital at 11.30 am and was welcomed by the Mayor Sutton, Alderman Andrew Letts.

Opening the pool, she congratulated the organisers on the 'wonderful results' they had obtained.

She had been very interested in visiting the hospital because of its outstanding reputation.

It was certainly unusual, she said, that a hospital the size of Queen Mary's should provide care for general cases, as well as psychiatric and handicapped patients.

Mr Richard Hearne then gave a short speech on behalf of 'Mr Pastry' who, he explained, was 'unfortunately unable to attend'.

"On behalf of the hundreds of brave little souls who will benefit from this pool, may I say – God bless you all."

by Robert Toyne

THE PULSE NO. 12 DECEMBER 1966

Poem

Queen Mary's Hospital is nice,
I hope it's a reasonable price.
Some patients are not very ill,
But if they are, they must be still.
They wake you up at twelve midnight,
To give you medicine which is right.
And then again at half past five.
It's a wonder that I'm still alive.
The nurses and doctors are helping me,
So I'm getting better as you can see.

by Rosemary Penn (aged 10, Ward B1)

Music Club

Every two weeks some of us go to Music Club to play our bamboo pipes. Many schools play recorders and some play bamboo pipes as we do. We think pipes have a sweeter sound.

When the boys first started going to Music Club – so I have heard – they used to have ginger biscuits and a cup of tea. Now we have a regular feast with sandwiches of all sorts; and ginger, chocolate, sponge and fruit cakes as well as savoury biscuits. All this is brought by kind 'Tea Ladies' – Mrs Silverstone and Mrs Seaby. Other friends come too. They also wash up and dry the dishes.

Now it seems to be Tea and Piping, when perhaps before it was Piping and Tea!

by Larry Barns

Words; Words; Words

Have you ever thought how often we will use our ability to read? It starts when we look at the daily paper in the morning, then we read of the latest free gift on our packet of cereals, or how to make up a cut-out model from the carton; if we go to a football match we read the programme to find out the team and even when we watch television we are constantly reading captions to get the full story.

Man learned to write – and read – almost as soon as he learned to live together and I have in my office a piece of stone with some writing on it from Ur, which experts say is six thousand years old – written long before the Flood! Just compare this with the latest in microfilms which the Men from UNCLE are constantly chasing – you can get two or three hundred pages of print these days on to a single 35mm frame to save space.

The smallest book made up of bound pages is a book of poetry, 'Poems of Edgar Guest', handwritten by an American called Burt Randle and it measures exactly one eighth of an inch square, fastened by a metal clasp and made in 1942.

The biggest book ever made is 'The Story of the South' printed, as you might expect, in the United States, and it is six feet ten inches high, twelve inches thick and nine feet two inches wide when it is open! It is equipped with a twelve horse-power motor to turn the leaves and bound in leather – the complete hide of one outsize Texan ox!

The biggest English book is an atlas in the British Museum library, six feet high and more than six feet wide when open.

People often complain today of the high price of books, but this very week a world record high price was paid for a manuscript - £90,000. Before this, a Gutenberg Bible held the record for value – bought by the Library of Congress in 1954 for £71,400 and this is thought nowadays to be worth about £107,000.

The world's best-seller was always the Bible until recent years but it was overtaken some time ago by the A.A. Handbook and now it is a book on bringing up children by Dr Spock 'Childcare'.

The power of the written word is still very great and there really is no telling to what remote places this little magazine will penetrate and in what strange circumstances some day someone will read it. Who knows, somebody, somewhere may read this who is already writing the book that will become the smallest, the largest, the rarest or even the most popular book the world has ever known!

by S. Dean

THE PULSE – APRIL 1969

Edna Coventry

Everyone who visited our school before Easter 1968 will have carried away an unforgettable impression of Mrs Coventry as a gracious, warm, deeply sympathetic personality, whose first thought was always for the wellbeing of her pupils and her staff.

It is therefore with a sense of deep personal loss that we have to report that on the evening of Monday, March 3rd, she passed peacefully away, after a protracted illness. During her last conscious moments, she spoke to the Ward Sister of this school about her happiness that its work was continuing.

Going on the Stage – by Ward C8

| *"Whom do you serve"* | *"Dick Whittington"* |
| Nativity | Pantomime |

As you look from the stage you feel a thrill of excitement passing through you. Lights of many colours would be shining on you, and for a moment there would be a tense atmosphere, until the first bar of music is played.

The audience would be in complete darkness, and as you say your words, or sing, or dance, you feel as if a thousand eyes are upon you.

As the first curtain is taken you feel sad. All is over, and although you might have felt scared at first, you had enjoyed it. Rushing around, dressing up in silly costumes, with beautiful head-dresses and funny masks and funny costumes.

The first play C8 did was the Nativity, after which we all felt a lot of hard work had been put into it.

Costumes had to be put aside, but another surprise awaited us, and it was to be a Pantomime and the best thought of all is making other people laugh. The Pantomime was made up of lots of funny characters, and it did not matter if anyone fell over by accident. It was all meant to be funny. And it was.

by Helen Wiggs and Alice Fitzwarren

It was funny that my first experience as an actress was at Queen Mary's Hospital. It was in a Nativity play in which I was a lady of the Court. I loved dressing up in a mauve silk dress. That was quite fun, but later we did a Pantomime called "Dick Whittington" which was much more fun.

I played four parts in the Pantomime. I was a lady of London, then a sailor, and then I and two other people did the horn pipe dance. Then I was a savage on a desert island that Dick was shipwrecked on, and there was more dancing, this time round a tree with three others.

The best person in it was Helen Wiggs who ended up being Dick's wife. Dick's good fairy was played by Yvonne Chapman who wore a lovely white fairy dress. David Young was also very good as the shop boy who was very lazy. Dick and Dick's cat were very amusing as they acted it very well indeed and made the audience laugh.

The rehearsals as well as the actual play were good fun. I think the play was as much fun for us as it was for the audience, judging by their laughter. Mr Michell produced the play, and acted extremely well.

Life on another planet
Is there life on another planet? I have been asked that question many times. Well, - I'll begin by telling you about some reports and then you can judge for yourself.

On the 30th June 1908, people living in a desolate part of Arctic Siberia saw a remarkable sight 'A great flame', much brighter than the sun appeared in the sky and after a few moments there was a noise which was described as being like an artillery barrage going on for several minutes. It was some time before anyone got there, but when they did they saw the area was a complete shambles. The trees had been blown down for twenty miles in each direction. They had no bark on at all and were scorched as though by a furnace and the most amazing thing was that over a thousand reindeer had been killed. Luckily at the time there was no-one there.

In 1948, forty years after the incident, a scientific meeting was held in Moscow and was addressed by a man called Dr Kasantseu, who had his own ideas on what happened. He really believed (so he said) that it was a space-ship from Mars! He said in his own words "The Martian left home in 1907 and arrived in 1908, but unfortunately their ship exploded. It was probably carrying explosives". The idea of the spaceship was so unlikely that they did not believe him.

But a tragic accident occurred at Fort Knox in America where Flying Officer Mantell saw a UFO (that means Unidentified Flying Object). He said "It (meaning the UFO) is twice the size of my craft (which was a Vulcan Bomber) ... going at tremendous speed ... am going to chase ... out." We don't know what happened but they found the plane scattered over a wide area and neither the parents nor his friends were allowed to see his body. Scientists claim that the weapon used must be very advanced.

There is also a project called OZMA after the imaginary land of OZ, a remote and inaccessible place. They (the scientists) are trying to communicate with intelligent beings. It is conducted by F. H. Drake, an American astronomer, who points a radio telescope at two planets and listens.

But there are definitely flying saucers. I remember seeing a book about a space-ship crash into a mountain and only killing a little man with red hair, only 23" tall.

by David Young, Ward C8

Poem

There was a small pup in the snow.
He never knew quite where to go.
So he hopped on a bus,
without any fuss,
And there goes old Fido you know.

by Audrey Fidler, Ward C8

EXTRACTS FROM PULSE
(Magazine of Queen Mary's Hospital School)

The Paris Visit

A trip to Paris really is the 'holiday of a lifetime' for the ten fortunate youngsters who are chosen every other year to spend eight days as the guests of the Hospital Raymond Poincare at Garches.

The chief criterion for their selection is that they should be young people for whom continental travel under private arrangements would be difficult or impossible.

In 1967 we took six pupils who are more or less permanently confined to wheelchairs and four more physically handicapped youngsters, all with a long history of hospitalisation behind them.

Thoughts of hospitals were far from our minds as we were helped up the stairs to the waiting Skyways jet prop plane that was to whirl us to Beauvais. Here the coach belonging to our hosts brought this every day. Then began a round of delight for our charges and of delight tempered with some hard work for the accompanying staff. We asked some of the party to record the day that they enjoyed most –

We got there on Monday and then we unpacked. In the evening we went to a Youth Club. I have never been to a Youth Club before.

Mary Louise Hewett, D1

The day I enjoyed most was Saturday July 15th. We all went shopping in the morning. The shops were lovely. After lunch we went for a marvellous cruise up the River Seine in a pleasure boat.

It was very hot and sunny and as we went under the bridges a guide told us all about their history in English and French. He told us about other buildings too.

Along the banks some people were asleep in the sun; there was one man fishing – and as we went under the bridges people waved to us.

Tina Dance, F3

As everyone knows, July the fourteenth is a great day in France – and it was a great day for us for we went to see the grand parade in the Champs Elysees.

It rained a little early in the morning but cleared before we left the hospital at 7.45 am after our French breakfast. We reached the Champs Elysees at about 8.30 am because we had to be in our seats in good time. Here is my invitation from General de Gaulle –

First a brigade of horsemen came galloping past – then a squadron of small French fighter planes flew overhead. They looked like our Red Arrows except that they were a little larger. Some heavier planes came next, zooming overhead. The procession continued with artillery and machine guns. The procession carried on for more than an hour.

LE GÉNÉRAL DE GAULLE
Président de la République Française

prie Monsieur *David Clarke*
de lui faire l'honneur d'assister à la cérémonie
qui aura lieu le 14 JUILLET 1967, à 9 heures,
avenue des Champs-Élysées, à l'occasion de la
Fête nationale.

VOIR AU VERSO LES CONDITIONS D'ACCÈS

After this interesting morning we spent the afternoon sight-seeing and in the evening we saw a firework display and the dancing in the streets at Bastille and Invalides Square.

David Clarke, F3

I enjoyed it very much at the theatre. We went on Sunday in the evening. The play was a very funny one and although it was in French we could understand parts of it and laughed in most of the right places. When we got back to the hospital it was bed straightaway after a new experience for most of us.

Denis Slater, Cerebral Palsy Unit

PULSE April 1969

What Makes Them Tick? The Pathology Laboratory

Your introduction to hospital was probably through an uncomfortable or even downright painful feeling. After being seen by the doctor and made comfortable by the nurses, who should come along but a technician from the laboratory with, apparently, the sole idea of increasing your discomfort. With a technique copied straight from a mosquito your thumb is pricked, a little blood is sucked up and stored away in one or two little tubes. This is probably all you actually see of the laboratory but we see rather more of you than you would believe. Not only does this little drop of blood come to us but so do the swabs which we take from your throat, or the drop of your water which is carefully collected into a small bottle, and the larger drop of blood which the doctor may take from your arm. Should you go to the theatre to have your tonsils or appendix taken out, these, too, will come over to us.

In the laboratory these "gifts" are distributed by our office to different groups of technicians each having a different name and job to do.

One group will handle all the swabs and similar specimens. This is called the Bacteriology Lab. and their job is to grow any germs which may be on the swab. For example, you may have a sore throat; if it is caused by a germ this will be grown, identified and tested with antibiotics such as penicillin. Your doctor can then be told the name of the germ causing your sore throat and which antibiotic will probably kill it to let your throat get better.

Another group looks after your blood. This is called the Haematology Lab. and you have probably met one of them collecting a small drop from you. As you know one of the main jobs your blood has is to fight any infection. The white blood cells, like any other army, are mobilised and different types of cell have different targets. By knowing which cells are increased the doctor can deduce what the target is - i.e. what sort of infection is being fought. Another of its jobs is to carry oxygen to the tissues - this is the function of the red blood cells which can be thought of as a transport section of the army. The laboratory can let the doctor know whether this section is operating properly or whether the lorries (cells) carrying the oxygen are short in numbers, damaged or not fully loaded. With this knowledge your doctor will know whether he needs to give you any special foodstuff to help you make more cells or to load them properly.

One more job which you have is to get rid of waste products and to keep your body chemicals balanced. Often when you don't feel well this is because your illness is slightly altering this delicate balance. The Biochemistry Lab. will test your blood and perhaps water to see that this balance is maintained and that waste products are being removed from your body. Another sort of test is to feed you with a known amount of food and to see how long it takes you to absorb it and to use it. The results of these tests will help your doctor to know whether you need any other medicines to help you feel better.

Sometimes, of course, you come to hospital to have an operation. Perhaps your appendix is inflamed and your doctor believes that you will feel better if it is removed. It may be something even smaller such as a mole in an awkward place. Once the theatre has removed it the Histology Lab. receives it, cuts very thin sections under a microscope. You can see that different tissue looks different - for example a piece of muscle looks different from a piece of skin. Under the microscope this architecture is more obvious and any alteration by disease can be seen and reported to your doctor.

You will probably have realised from this that many of the tests may have to be done more than once - first to find out what is wrong and again to make sure that you are getting better. It might even mean coming back to see us in Out Patients, but at least you soon know that we are trying to help your doctor to keep you well.

Music Therapy

A T.V. free-lance team came in October to film a group of us making music with bamboo pipes, a glockenspiel and a metaliophone. They arrived at about ten o'clock with all their gear and stayed for about one and a half hours filming us in colour! We were asked to play some Music before-hand so for about two or three weeks we played and played, and they picked the easiest one of all! But it was just as well because it took us an hour and a bit. Miss Alvin played her cello for us, we all though she played very well.

Deborah Cool

DR LAWSON
AND
MR PERONA-WRIGHT

DR DAVID LAWSON – PHYSICIAN SUPERINTENDENT
MR K G PERONA-WRIGHT FCIS, FHA – GROUP SECRETARY

The following two articles give an insight into the range of work carried out by staff at Queen Mary's. Dr Lawson and Mr Perona-Wright give a brief resumé of the hospital, before providing figures showing the different medical conditions treated, and beds allocated for each illness.

Queen Mary's Hospital Clinical Services
David Lawson, Physician Superintendent   7/1/55

The Hospital was built in the early years of the century at Carshalton on the Surrey Downs, on a 136 acre site which had been bought from the Stanley estates. It was originally intended for use as a convalescent fever hospital for the London area, but was never used for this purpose.

The Hospital was opened in 1909 by John Burns, who was then President of the Local Government Board, as the "Children's Infirmary"; its purpose was to relieve the pressure of the accommodation for the sick poor of the Metropolis "to bring them" as John Burns put it in his opening address, "out of the workhouses and on to the breezy downs of Surrey".

A few years after the opening Royal Patronage was granted and the Hospital was re-named QUEEN MARY'S HOSPITAL FOR CHILDREN. It was managed by the Metropolitan Asylum Board until, following the Local Government Act of 1929, it was transferred to the London County Council, in whose hands it remained until the inception of the National Health Service in 1948.

During this time a reputation was steadily built up for the handling and teaching of all long stay cases, particularly in the large units devoted to tuberculous and other orthopaedic cases, poliomyelitis and rheumatic fever.

In 1912 verandas were added to ten of the single storey ward blocks; and between 1928 and 1930 a chapel, two further single storey ward blocks, and four nurses homes were built.

Until 1948 the Hospital served the London area only, and had few ties with the rapidly increasing population of the immediately surrounding area. When the Hospital was taken over by the National Health service in July 1948, it was constituted as a single Hospital Group, under the South west Metropolitan regional Hospital Board.

Since that time steady progress has been made in building up not only the long stay services for which the hospital had already become famous, but also the other services and departments necessary for the provision of a full range of modern paediatric services, including acute medicine and surgery.

The Hospital is not now limited in the geographical area from which it may draw cases and is capable of providing all the paediatric services required for a large area of Surrey, and for certain special purposes from a much wider area. It is also a major centre for the training of paediatric nurses. In the last ten years the problems of nursing recruitment have been solved, and there is now no difficulty in recruiting any nursing staff required.

A School is run by the Surrey County Council within the Hospital as an integral part of the Hospital service, staffed by forty-five trained teachers. The great majority of the teaching is done on the wards. This service, quite apart from its value in continuing the children's education, is of the greatest clinical value in maintaining the morale of intermediate and long stay cases.

The Hospital has 840 beds. Nearly all the wards are single storey U shaped blocks with a courtyard on the south side of the building, on which all the beds can be put in suitable weather. Some of the wards have covered balconies running round the courtyard, and the children in these wards can stay outside throughout the twenty-four hours.

The Hospital provides a full range of medical and surgical paediatric services for babies and children of all ages up to 16, including the following general and special units:-

Acute medical and surgical wards, including a neonatal surgical unit

Cerebral palsy

Clinical laboratories

Dental (orthodontics)

Ear, nose and throat surgery, including a special unit for the testing and treatment of deafness

Gastro-enteritis

Ophthalmic

Orthopaedics, including acute and long-stay cases, and surgical tuberculosis

Poliomyelitis - cases are admitted at the onset of the disease and continuity of treatment and education can be maintained as long as may be necessary

Rheumatism, chorea and rheumatoid arthritis

X-ray

CONSULTANT STAFF

Those marked * are available for domiciliary visits.

Physician Superintendent	*Dr. David Lawson	Wallington 6635
Anaesthetist	Dr. D. C. Howard	
Dental Surgeon	Mr. Antony Westbrook	
Dermatologist	*Dr. Bentley Phillips	Ewell 6323
Ear, Nose and		
Throat Surgeons	*Mr L. G. Kingdom	Uplands 2876
	Mr. R. H. Welch	
	Miss Whetnall	
Gynaecologist and		
Venereologist	Miss G. M. Sandes	
Neurologist	*Dr. Blake Pritchard	Welbeck 6433
Orthalmic Surgeon	Miss E. D. L. Simpson	
Orthopaedic Surgeons	*Mr. R. H. Metcalfe	Uplands 8566
	Mr. R. G. Thomas	
Pathologist	Dr. G. T. Stewart	

Physicians	*Dr. J. Nuttal Horne	Vigilant 0902
	*Dr. C. W. Kesson	Ashtead 3562
	*Dr. David Lawson	Wallington 6635
Radiologists	Dr. N. D. W. Morrison	
	*Dr. B. C. H. Ward	Lee Green 2592
Surgeons	Dr. Denis Browne	
	*Mr. H. H. Nixon	Beckenham 0273
Urological Surgeon	Mr. J. G. Yates Bell	

ADMISSION ARRANGEMENTS

For <u>urgent</u> admissions telephone Wallington 6635. Arrangements similar to those in use by the Emergency Bed Service are in force to ensure that doctors are not kept waiting for a reply. Requests for admission and transfer of lesser urgency are more conveniently dealt with by letter addressed to the Physician Superintendent.

Mothers are admitted to Hospital with their babies whenever this is advisable.

VISITING TIMES

| Wednesday and Friday | 5.00 pm to 5.30 pm |
| Sunday | 2.00 pm to 4.00 pm |

Special permission for visiting more frequently or at other times is given when appropriate. Visiting by children is not normally allowed. An exception is made in the case of visits to children who have been in Hospital for more than six months; these visits are arranged at other than normal visiting times.

Visiting by family doctors of their cases in Hospital is welcomed, but such visits should preferably be made by appointment so that the House Officer can arrange to be in attendance.

DISCHARGE OF PATIENTS

Not later than the day of discharge, a brief note is sent to the doctor by the House officer, stating that the child is being discharged, giving the diagnosis, and also any advice about management which the family doctor will need to know in advance of receiving the clinical summary. Further copies of summaries are available to other doctors who may be concerned in the management of the case, on application.

Cases are followed up after discharge in Out-Patients where appropriate, and a further letter is sent to the family doctor after the final visit.

TRANSPORT
The Hospital is ten minutes walk from Carshalton Beeches Station, from which it is approached by the way of Crichton Road and Queen Mary's Avenue. There are frequent trains from Victoria and London Bridge via West Croydon and Holborn Viaduct via Wimbledon and Sutton. There is a taxi rank at the Station.

The Hospital bus collects from Carshalton Beeches Station at 10.10 am and 2.10 pm daily and also at 10.40 am on Mondays and Thursdays. Return journeys are run as required.

Omnibus services:-

Route 213 Kingston - Belmont	Alight at Stanley Park Road (5 minutes walk) or at Carshalton Beeches Station.

Other Bus routes:-

470 Dorking - Warlingham 408 Guildford - Warlingham 725 Windsor - Gravesend 654 Sutton - Crystal Palace	Alight at the "Windsor Castle" which is on the 213 bus route and is five minutes walk from Carshalton Beeches Station.
234 Wallington - Selsdon 234a Hackbridge - Purley	Alight at Wallington Station - frequent trains to Carshalton Beeches.

The hospital's own vehicles are used to supplement public transport services and anyone with special transport problems or a difficult journey is requested to telephone the Hospital, Wallington 6635, and ask for advice.

EDUCATION

A school is run by the Surrey Education Committee and is an integral part of the Hospital. The staff are qualified to teach children at all stages of development from Nursery to the General Certificate of Education level. The teachers of children suffering from Cerebral Palsy and Deafness have additional qualifications. Teaching is given on the wards to all children who are confined to bed, and who are able to profit from education. This applies not only to long-stay cases but to all children whose stay in the Hospital is prolonged for a sufficient period of time to make education advisable. Contact is kept with the children's ordinary school. Special arrangements are made where necessary, for children to take external examinations, such as Common Entrance examination and the General Certificate of Education, while they are in Hospital. The school curriculum includes weekly educational films and a travelling library.

LABORATORY SERVICES FOR THE FAMILY DOCTOR

Services of a routine nature are available; arrangements should be made with the Pathologist who will send his report direct to the Doctor concerned, but may refer cases needing urgent attention to one of his clinical colleagues in the Hospital.

X-RAY SERVICES FOR THE FAMILY DOCTOR

It is hoped that the re-equipment of the Department will shortly enable the Hospital to offer services direct to doctors outside the hospital.

CLINICAL MEETINGS are held at the Hospital on Sunday mornings once a month, to which all doctors are welcome.

NURSING

The training at this Hospital is for the Registered Sick Children's Nurse's Certificate and covers a period of three years, during which time nurses gain experience in every field of children's nursing. Students must be eighteen years of age before they can commence training and are expected to have a good standard of general education, preferably with the General Certificate of Education. Students spend the first three months of their training in the Preliminary Training School and return to the lecture room for study periods at intervals throughout their training.

THE DENTAL DEPARTMENT is fully equipped to care for the dental health of children admitted to the Hospital, who are routinely examined by the dental Surgeon shortly after admission. Out-patient facilities are also available for the following purposes:-

(1) Orthodontics and the provision of appliances
(2) Radiographs
(3) Implantations
(4) Cases in respect of which a second opinion is required

Dental Beds are available for surgical extraction, the treatment of impacted or buried teeth, and for any other purposes for which admission to Hospital is advisable.

OUT-PATIENT DEPARTMENT

Children on whom a Consultant's opinion is required can be seen by appointment on the following days on application by the patient's doctor to the Physician Superintendent. This application should normally be in writing, but when the case is urgent an appointment can be arranged over the telephone, as for acute admissions. Emergencies and casualties will be seen at any time.

Cerebral Palsy Diagnostic Clinic	Tuesday morning	Dr. Lawson Mrs. Collis
Dermatology	By appointment	Dr. Bentley Phillips
Ear, Nose and Throat	Monday afternoon Thursday afternoon Friday morning	Miss Whetnall Mr. Kingdom Mr. Welch
Medicine	Monday morning Thursday morning Friday morning	Dr. Kesson Dr. Lawson Dr. Horne
Neurology	By appointment	Dr. Blake Pritchard
Ophthalmology	Thursday morning	Miss Simpson

Orthodontics	Tuesday morning	Mr. Westbrook
	Tuesday afternoon	
	Thursday morning	
	Friday morning	
Orthopaedics	Monday morning	Mr. Thomas
	Thursday morning	Mr. Metcalfe
Surgery	Monday afternoon	Mr. Nixon
Urology	By appointment	Mr. Yate Bell
Venereology	By appointment	Miss Sandes

FOUNTAIN AND CARSHALTON GROUP HOSPITAL MANAGEMENT COMMITTEE

Queen Mary's Hospital For Children, Carshalton, Surrey

Chairman: The Lord Grenfell, T.D.
Group Secretary: K. G. Perona-Wright, F.C.I.S., F.H.A.

Queen Mary's was first opened in 1909 as a long stay childrens' hospital and between 1948 and 1959 became a general childrens' hospital, treating all childrens' illnesses, both acute and chronic. Its present name dates from a visit by Her Late Majesty, Queen Mary in 1914.

In 1959 the Fountain Hospital for Mentally Handicapped children was transferred to this site and amalgamated with Queen Mary's, thus forming the first comprehensive childrens' hospital in the United Kingdom, in accordance with the intentions of the Mental Health Act 1959 to bring an end to the historical isolation of mental and physical illness, in the hospital service.

Accordingly, of the 726 beds of the hospital, the allocation is made up as follows:-

60   acute surgical beds (including eye and dental surgery and spina bifida patients)
100 acute medical beds
20   isolation beds
20   long stay medical beds
30   beds for ear, nose and throat cases
60   beds for orthopaedic cases
30   beds for miningomyelocele cases
20   beds for cerebral palsy cases
30   beds for muscular dystrophy cases
16   beds for emotionally disturbed children

The balance of 340 beds, each in 20 bedded wards are for mentally Handicapped patients. A new service is being provided by using a small number of these beds for Day Hospital care.

In the past few years the following additions to the hospital have been made:-

- an enclosed swimming pool for therapeutic and recreational purposes.
- an architect designed Pets Corner
- a block of 4 flatlets which enable children who cannot go home to be given some idea of family life by living in a flatlet with their parents, or to be used when the child is to be discharged or the parents need to learn to use certain special equipment.
- A Friends' Centre, i.e. a canteen and social centre run by our League of Friends
- a Sports Pavilion with a heated open-air swimming pool for the use of the staff
- a school containing 10 classrooms, 8 of which are for mentally handicapped children and 2 for the use of paediatric patients.

For many years the hospital has had a block containing 9 bedrooms in which mothers can stay overnight if the child needs his mother, or comes for assessment from too great a distance for return journey to be feasible the same day.

The hospital contains a special school for the paediatric patients, consisting of a headmaster and 30 teachers who can teach normal children the full range of primary and secondary education. In addition two teachers have classes for 8 autistic/ psychotic children. These teachers are employed by the local Education Authority. The hospital, out of its own budget also employs a trained teacher as Organiser and approximately 12 supervisors to educate mentally handicapped children. Of the 340 mentally handicapped children 100 are capable of attending this school on a daily basis, together with around 20 daily children residing at home.

The hospital has approximately 450 nurses in training; of these about 250 study for the Certificate in Sick Children Nursing (RSCN). The other 200 nurses are studying for the Certificate in Nursing the Children with Learning Difficulties (RNMS).

The hospital contains its own Chapel and has a resident Anglican Chaplain. Ministers of other denominations visit regularly. There is a Miniature Railway. A number of children, mainly mentally handicapped, have regular riding lessons arranged free by the Riding for the Disabled Group.

The Pathology department, in addition to its routine work, carries out a considerable research programme and provides a Regional Infant Screening Service for Phenylketonuria.

Medical and psychological research into many physical and mental diseases is in progress and an increase in research into mental handicap will result when the Institute for Mental Retardation, financed by the National Society for Mentally Handicapped Children, is established in the hospital grounds within the next few years. Already several hundred visitors of many disciplines and nationalities come to see the work of the hospital annually.

THE FOUNTAIN HOSPITAL

Main entrance to the hospital and the fountain

The fountain in the front drive of the Hospital represents a child carrying a tortoise. This symbolises the handicap of mental retardation. It is the function of the Fountain Group of Hospitals to help carry this burden and, by training and encouragement, to fit as many children as possible for life in the community.

EDITH LOUISA CAVELL

Edith Cavell was born in Norfolk on December 4th 1865. She did her nurse training at the Fountain Hospital, situated in Tooting, South London.

Following her training, Edith Cavell became Matron of the Berkendael Medical Institute in Brussels which had become a Red Cross Hospital, and during the German occupation harboured wounded and refugee soldiers and aided their escape into Holland. Denounced by a renegade, she was tried by court martial on October 7th 1915, and despite neutral mediation was shot five days afterwards.

Edith Cavell's remains now repose in Norwich Cathedral; a memorial statue stands in St Martin's Lane, London.

NB: A Belgian, Philippe Baucqo, provided the soldiers with money and guides.

"I have seen death so often that it is not strange or painful to me. I am glad to die for my country."
BRUSSELS, *October 12th*, 1915.

Photographs of Edith Cavell have been kindly contributed by the RCN (Archives) Edinburgh

The Memorial Statue in
St Martin's Lane, London
- picture contributed by
RCN (Archives) Edinburgh

Patriotism is not enough

"Standing, as I do, in the view of God and Eternity,
I realise that patriotism is not enough.
I must have no hatred or bitterness towards anyone."

Edith Cavell, (about to be shot)

The Tongues of Dying Men

O But they say the tongues of dying men
Enforce attention like deep harmony:
Where words are scarce they are seldom spent in vain,
For they breathe truth that breathe their words in pain.

from King Richard II by William Shakespeare

1652

The Metropolitan Asylums Board.

FEVER HOSPITAL

APPLICATION FOR THE APPOINTMENT OF ASSISTANT NURSE, CLASS II.

1. Name in full
2. Address
3. Age *30*
4. Height
5. If married, or a widow, number of children
6. Where educated
7. Present engagement, length of service, annual salary, and other emoluments

I have had no hospital training.
Nor any nursing experience whatever.

8. Previous engagements, viz —

9. Particulars as to training —
   (a) Name and address of Hospital or Poor Law Infirmary
   (b) Duration of training — From
   To

Signature of Candidate

Dec. 6th 1895

This copy of Edith Cavell's application to the Fountain Hospital for her nurse training was kindly contributed by former Fountain and Queen Mary's nurse Brenda Elliot.

181

The Development and Present Position of a Psychiatric Hospital - The Fountain Hospital, SW17

Iris Niekerk
Brenda Whittle

The awakening social conscience of the middle nineteenth century prompted an awareness of the nation's responsibility to it's multitudinous poor. The Metropolitan Asylums Board was established in 1867, the off-spring of the Metropolitan Poor Act of the same year. This Act gave power to the Poor Law Board to establish "asylums" for the infirm, insane and sick; the Metropolitan Asylums District included all the unions and parishes of London.

A cholera outbreak in 1893 precipitated the erection in eight weeks of a temporary hospital of 384 beds originally intended to stand 10 years. This was the Fountain Hospital, built at Tooting Graveney, one of Surrey's smallest parishes, in an area which was still little more than a village, where the main road to Epsom was still unmade, sending up clouds of dust in summer, and becoming a quagmire in winter. This temporary cluster of corrugated iron huts, lined with uralite, and painted within and without continued in use until March 1963, and it is on this site that the new St. George's Hospital will be built. The Metropolitan Asylums Board initially administered the Fountain Hospital through its Hospitals committee, which managed the infectious diseases hospitals, but in 1910 the patients were transferred to the new Grove Fever Hospital, and the Fountain Hospital was opened as a temporary measure to accommodate patients with learning difficulties for one year. The Asylums Committee then assumed responsibility, and acted for the Board until the Local Government Act of 1929 transferred this responsibility to the London County Council.

The use of the Fountain Hospital for mentally defective patients was a result of the proposed Mental Deficiency Act of 1913. Prior to this Act idiots and imbeciles had been dealt with under the Idiots Act of 1886 and the Lunacy Act of 1890; but the largest group - the adult feeble-minded were not recognised by law, and therefore there was no legal provision of care, supervision or control for them, unless they were certified as "of unsound mind".

It was a currently held belief at this period that the nation would degenerate if "feeble-minded" persons - a term applied to social misfits as well as to those of defective mind - were allowed to reproduce: hence the pressure to segregate these people from the community, and the resulting Mental Deficiency Act of 1913, which gave this power. Education for mentally defective children was not compulsory, although permitted by the Defective and Epileptic Children (Education) Act of 1899. However, since 1897 the Metropolitan Asylums Board had been responsible for providing accommodation for Poor Law children who "by reason of defect of intellect.... cannot properly be trained in association with children in ordinary schools". The board appear to have been advanced in their approach to this problem, and set up small units throughout London, where children were cared for by a house-mother, leading a home life as near normal as possible, and attending special schools. by 1911 the expected success from this scheme not being forth-coming (and possibly with an eye to economy) the Board decided it could be more efficient to detain feeble-minded children in large colonies, rather than in small scattered homes.

It was ultimately decided to group the boards institutions, and certify them for treatment under the 1913 Act. Darenth Training Colony and Bridge Training home were to receive improvable juveniles, Leavesdon and Caterham Mental Hospital to receive idiot children.

The Board of Control was established under the 1913 Mental Deficiency Act, and empowered to inspect institutions caring for mental defectives. The Commissioners reported on 5th June, 1914, that they had inspected "all parts" of the Fountain Hospital, which was shortly to be "disused for its present purpose, the Board having purchased as a substitute the Strand Union Workhouse at Edmonton". the outbreak of World War I two months later halted these plans, and the all too familiar post war building restrictions resulted in the hospital still being in use for its "purpose" in 1929, when it's administration passed to the London County Council. The depression and unfavourable economic conditions of the 1930's delayed rebuilding, whilst hospital bed occupancy rose to 826 by 1938, and at the outbreak of the 1939 war, 890 mentally defective patients were being cared for.

The patients remained throughout the 1940 London Blitz, damage from a fire bomb, a high explosive bomb, and an anti-aircraft shell being suffered. It was not until a flying bomb completely destroyed one quarter of the hospital in 1944 that the beds were reduced to 680, for three wards had been completely destroyed. History repeated itself and so the aftermath of war again prevented rebuilding. At the same time numbers rose to 720.

On July 5th, 1948, the Fountain ceased to be administered by the London County Council, through a sub-committee of the Mental Hospitals committee. On this date three hospitals; the Fountain Hospital, South Side Home, Streatham, and Ellen Terry Home, Reigate were united under one Management Committee. South Side Home, previously untenanted, was opened as a hostel for 80 adult-female patients, and this reduced the numbers at Tooting to 650. Ellen Terry Home, previously voluntarily supported by the Servers of the Blind League, is the only home of its kind in this country caring for blind children with learning difficulties.

Over the years the Fountain Hospital had used it's unique position, as the only hospital caring purely for children with learning difficulties, to pioneer new ideas into treatment of such children, to initiate research, and encourage wider public interest in this field. New specialist departments evolved after the second world war to cope with this wider aspect of the function of the hospital; Departments of Psychology and Clinical Research; X-ray, Dental, Physiotherapy, Pharmacy, Neuro-Pathology, Bio-chemistry, Social Welfare, Medical Records, Speech Therapy and Out-Patients Departments. It was obvious the hospital had outgrown the 1893, 384 bedded unit, and a planning committee including doctors and nurses met to exchange ideas and plan a new hospital. Two ministers of health visited the crumbling hospital, inspected cracked walls, inadequate facilities and overcrowded wards.

Eventually the Minister decided that the Fountain Hospital and Queen Mary's Hospital for Children, Carshalton, should unite to become the first comprehensive hospital, caring for physically sick and children with learning difficulties. The two existing Management Committees were dissolved, and a new Fountain and Queen Mary's Hospital Management Committee established in October, 1959. Disused wards at Carshalton were re-decorated and new sanitary annexes built.

Patients from the Fountain Hospital were transferred to these 20 bedded units as they became available. Meanwhile St. Ebba's Hospital, Epsom was being converted to receive adult patients, so that by 31st March, 1963 the Fountain Hospital at Tooting was closed. There are sixteen wards in use at Queen Mary's for children with learning difficulties, but only 320 patients.

A hospital is judged by the spirit which emanates from it, rather than from the building it inhabits. Physically, the Fountain Hospital consisted of 16 pavilions built in pairs on either side of a covered corridor. Each ward originally had 40 beds, and was separated from its neighbour by grass or an "airing court". An official of the Metropolitan Asylums Board reported in 1920 that the buildings were well suited to their purpose, easy to keep clean and easy to administer, and in summer most of the meals could be taken out of doors. In recent years, from personal experience it can be stated that the sanitary annexes were quite inadequate; two baths in which to bath 50 or even 60 patients, and four or five toilets for the same number of ambulant children. Some of the present day Sisters remember when Ward Sisters lived in bed-sitting rooms attached to the wards.

In its early years the most common admissions were paralysed and epileptic and the first concern was to rid the hair of vermin and heal the attendant skin diseases, a reflection of the social conditions of the time. The children were classified, but allocated to the wards so that the work was evenly distributed; evidence that medical and nursing liaison was well established. The response of these low grade children with learning difficulties to loving care and habit training was such that their improvement necessitated the inauguration of a school in 1917, and a "suitable teacher-nurse" was selected for the work.

Her programme of training was similar to that used to-day. She taught through play and musical games, and as her pupils progressed she introduced elementary kindergarten methods. This branch of training became an integral part of the hospital, and over the years men and women, especially trained to teach children with learning difficulties have taken over this responsibility from the "teacher nurses". However, the need for nurses to have experience in this aspect of nursing care has always been recognised, and nurses in training spend a period of time in the Children's School. Since the development of the comprehensive hospital at Queen Mary's, the School has been officially called the Fountain School to perpetuate this name.

Prior to 1948 the Medical Superintendent was responsible for the day to day administration of the hospital and, after the appointed day, he continued to serve the hospital as Physician Superintendent. It is noted in a report of 1920-21, that the Matron and her assistant were specially trained in the care and training of children, and that many of the sisters were trained children's nurses, and that the nurses were carefully selected because of their interest in this work.

A special booklet entitled "An Introduction to the Nursing and Care of the Mentally defective", Was issued by the London County Council, being a "Training Course for Probationer Nurses during the first six months' service and for hospital assistants in institutions for the mentally defective". Nurses were prepared for the Final Examination of the Royal Medical- Psychological association, and in later years for the certificate of the General Nursing Council.

Edith Cavell commenced training at the Fountain Hospital in December, 1895 when it was a fever hospital. She was thirty years old, and it was her first experience of hospital life - apparently not a happy one, as she left after nine months. In reading reports covering many years constant reference is made to the happy atmosphere of this hospital, and appreciation of the loving care given under very difficult circumstances.

The Nurses Training School is now well established, and since November 1957 the new experimented syllabus has been in use. Student nurses gain experience in sick children nursing, by spending eight weeks on the paediatric wards. Adult experience is gained at the Royal Earlswood Hospital. The period of training is three years, and post registration students are accepted for training over a shorter period.

The wards are staffed on the two shift system, a Ward Sister or Charge Nurse being in charge on each shift, several wards having both a Ward Sister and a Charge Nurse, so establishing a mother and father substitute.

In 1955 an annual study day for Ward Sisters was instituted, and was very successful. A Nursing Advisory Committee had been operating for several years, being reported in the Annual Report of 1949. Trained staff were sent on courses to the Royal College of Nursing and King Edwards Hospital Fund. In October 1948 a hospital magazine appeared for the first time, being prepared, printed and collated within the hospital. This magazine has recently changed its format, and is now the organ of the new comprehensive hospital, called "The Fountain".

Direct Admissions	1950	1951	1952	1953	1954	Total
Under Order (Section 6)	18	9	13	13	0	53
Placed by Patient (Section 3)	95	47	108	60	62	372
Temporary (Circular 5/52)	3	8	36	74	45	166
Totals	116	64	157	147	107	591

Children Admitted to Fountain Hospital

Each year the medical staff of the hospital are involved in an active teaching programme. Doctors, medical students, psychologists, social workers, nurses, teachers and many specialists from home and overseas visit the hospital, and programmes for one day, one week, or longer are planned and presented.

One of the major changes in recent years was the passing of the Mental Health Act, 1959, which replaced the Lunacy and Mental Treatment Acts, 1890 to 1930, and the Mental Deficiency Acts, 1913 to 1938, dissolved the Boards of Control and set up new legislation regarding mentally defective persons. It redefined and classified mental disorder, so that the old terms of idiot, imbecile and feeble-minded were replaced by the new terms sub-normal, severely sub-normal and psychopathic disorder with subsequent new definitions.

Members of the Management Committee, the Physician Superintendent, in 1957 "the early use of Section 3 (placement by parent) instead of Section 6 (Detention under order), temporary admission, informal admission, hostel environment, maximum licence, early discharge and community care have all been encouraged and developed, usually before they were generally accepted elsewhere and sometimes before they had been authorised (as in the case of temporary care and informal admissions".

A possible result of this experience was the publication of a Ministry of Health Circular in January 1958 (H.M. 58/5) announcing that informal admission was to be regarded as the normal mode of admission, and this was possible without amending legislation. Parents had been encouraged for some time to place their children under section 3 of the Act, rather than by order of the magistrate, and in 1954 all patients were admitted in this way and none under order. Much had been done to return the patient to the community, by placing the older ones in suitable employment, watching and assisting their progress and finally discharging them.

To this end a hostel was opened at Streatham in 1958. Children who were found to be able to benefit from special schools were transferred to E.S.N. schools, deaf schools and special schools for the handicapped. It was essential to the success of much of this work that there should be close co-operation between parents and hospital. This co-operation was fostered by encouraging parents to visit and take home their children on daily, weekend or longer leave.

The Fountain Hospital was the first Mental Deficiency Hospital to have a Friends or Parents Group, and this was the foundation of the National Society for Mentally Handicapped Children, to which the Hospital League of Friends is affiliated. The League of Friends has always been active in fund raising, to provide children with extra amenities: toys and records for the wards, Christmas ward parties and visits from Father Christmas. Attendance at the circus and pantomime are regular features of hospital life.

A new innovation after the last war was the establishment of a pets' corner so that children could become familiar with animals such as rabbits, chickens, pigeons, pigs, geese and goats, an experience denied to institutionalised patients. Since 1951 Osborne House, Hastings, a unit for 46 trainable adolescent boys has been a holiday home for patients from the other units, groups of twenty, with their own nurses spending a fortnight there during the summer.

Today the Fountain Hospital is part of a comprehensive hospital, actively participating in the new concept of mental health adumbrated in the Mental Health Act, 1959 and in the Nation Health Service Act. These last four years have been years of change and adaptation to new surroundings and a new concept of the comprehensive approach to paediatrics.

THE DEVELOPMENT AND ADMINISTRATION OF FOUNTAIN HOSPITAL - 1893 to present day

1893 - F. H. built as temporary   METROPOLITAN ASYLUMS
Fever Hospital   BOARD Hospital Committee

1910 - Patients transferred to
Grove Fever Hospital

1911 - F.H. re-opened temporarily   Asylums Committee (of M.A.B.)
for mental defective

1929   LONDON COUNTY COUNCIL
Sub - Committee of Mental
Hospitals Committee

1948 - Grouped with:
South Side Home, Streatham S. W. METROPOLITAN
REGIONAL HOSPITAL
BOARD
Ellen Terry Home, Reigate   Fountain Group Hospital
Management Committee

1952 - Osborne House, Hastings

1954 - Brooklands Home, Reigate

1958 - The Turret, Streatham

1959 - The Fountain Hospital and   Fountain and Carshalton Hospital
Queen Mary's Hospital   Management Committee
for Children, Carshalton merge

Bibliography

Mental Health Services   F.B. Mathews
Mental Deficiency   A.F. Tredgold
Mental Deficiency   L.T. Hilliard and B.H. Kirman
Mental Health Act, 1959

Official Memoranda. Metropolitan Asylums Board, 1902
Annual Report, Metropolitan Asylums Board, 1917 and 1920-21
Fountain Group Hospital Management Committee Annual Reports, 1949 and 1954-59
Fountain and Carshalton Group Hospital Management Committee Annual Reports, 1959-62
History of Tooting Graveney (published 1897)   W.E. Morden
Days that are Gone   A.J. Hurley

The Ellen Terry Home at Reigate consists of Terry House, the school Building, and Daffodil House. The home provides care and training for 50 mentally handicapped children who are also blind.

Some people do not realise that many children with learning difficulties can learn to do useful things and behave normally in many ways.

The Turret Hostel, recently opened in Streatham provides 20 beds for less handicapped homeless women who are able to work daily in local factories and restaurants for normal wages. These contribute towards their board and lodging.

Prizes and certificates are awarded each December, to commemorate the day Nurse Cavell started her nursing career at the Fountain in 1895, when it was a fever hospital.

Senior staff participate in T.W.I. (Training within Industry) Courses.

A playground has been made on part of the bomb site and there is a pets corner to instruct and amuse the children.

Special investigation is given to children who are paralysed or deaf, so that they may receive the appropriate training and education. Psychologists and speech therapists are members of staff.

Backward children, like normal children, need opportunities to develop their capacities to the maximum. Varied experiences and free play are as important as formal training.

Extracts from
THE FOUNTAIN – JULY/AUGUST 1962

THE BULLETIN OF THE FOUNTAIN AND CARSHALTON GROUP OF HOSPITALS

The official News Supplement of the Queen Mary's Hospital Staff Club

PAGE 1 – NEWS AND VIEWS

The new Executive Committee, elected by a postal ballot of staff, have now met twice, and have drawn up a Form of Constitution. This has been sent out to all staff, in readiness for the First General Meeting, which is to be held on Tuesday, 11th September, 1962 in the Recreation Hall, at 9 pm. A social evening will precede (8 pm) and follow the General Meeting. After formal adoption of the Constitution, the Club will be officially "in being" and can commence its work. An Inaugural Dance is being held from 8 pm to 12 midnight and full details will be publicised well in advance.

The new Committee elected its first officers as follows:

Chairman: Dr. BCH Ward (Consultant Radiologist)
Vice-Chairman: Mr G Hodson (Group Laundry Manager)
Hon. Secretary: Mr R Connington (Assistant to Group Secretary)
Hon. Treasurer: Mr J Waring (Finance Dept.)

The other members of the Committee are:

Miss Grubb (Principal Tutor), Mr Edwardson (Principal Tutor), Miss A Pitson and Miss T Page (Student Nurses), Mr W Blanks (Foreman Motor Mechanic), Mr S Ward (Transport Officer), Mr B Morris (Porter), Mr Bates (Art Master, Q M School).

It is good to report that the other clubs already in existence in the hospital have agreed to join the new club, and they will receive such financial and other support as they may require. It is hoped that in the future new activities may be started to provide facilities and interest for all members of all ages.

The next issue of "News and Views" will contain more definite information following the official "launching" of the new club.

Advance News

The club has been able to book a local hall for a Grand Carnival New Year's Eve Dance. Full details later.

Work on the new Sports Pavilion has commenced, and the staff Club, with the approval of the Hospital Management Committee, hope to be able to make good use of the facilities it will provide.

A competition is being organised among members for designs for a club badge, tie and scarf. Full details will be given in the next edition of "News and Views".

PAGE 11 – CHURCH NEWS

The Children's Harvest Thanksgiving Service this year at Queen Mary's will be held at 9.45 am on Sunday, September 16th, and will be conducted by the Rev. Francis Nelson Wright, Chaplain of Durlstone Court School, Barton-on-Sea, who last August was locum here for the Rev. E Noel-Cox and is a very old friend of his.

Hospital Sunday comes on October 14th, the Sunday preceding the Feast of St. Luke, Evangelist and Physician. At the special service at 3 pm, the Right Reverend James Virvos, Bishop of Apameia and Greek Orthodox Chaplain to the Hospital, has kindly consented to preach. Seats will be reserved for members of the nursing and other resident staff, who, if convenient, should wear their uniform.

United Prayer for our Group of Hospitals, our staff and our patients, is now offered every Wednesday in the chapel and is led by various people. Every department has promised to keep the Chaplain regularly informed of their needs.

PAGE 12 – THE FRENCH HOLIDAY
(A Prize-winning essay by "Taffy" of Ward E.10)

We had been looking forward to the French holiday for many weeks and we were very excited when the 13th June finally came. A great deal of preparation had to be made before everything was finally settled. There were our passports to be seen to, we had to have our photographs taken, details of where we were born, our height, the colour of our eyes, and a great many other things. Miss Nicolls came down to the ward and explained the foreign currency, and we made a list of prices in English money and put the equivalent in French. Seeing to our clothes was another detail. We made sure that all the buttons were sewn securely and that there were no tears or rips in them. Miss Gravell also went out and bought us notebooks so that we could make notes. So in all we had quite a busy time, even before the holiday began.

On Tuesday the old Hospital coach came to take our luggage down to Newhaven so that there would not be too much to take down on Wednesday morning. Tuesday night came at last and we all knew that we would not sleep much that night; and sure enough, at 5.30 am the next morning we were awake and waiting for the orderlies to come on duty and get us up. We were ready by 7.30 am and longing to make a start, but the coach did not appear! At last at 8 am the coach arrived and we were pushed into our places in the new coach and strapped in. We drove to the patients' kitchen; here we were seen off by Matron, Dr Lawson and a few other people. Finally, at 8.30 am we left the Hospital. The people who were coming with us on the holiday were – Mr and Mrs Joseph and their daughter, Deborah, Mr Reynolds, Mr Muller, Miss Whipp, the Almoner, Mrs Lawson, Miss Whittle and Nurse Tidd. The patients – Tommy, Richard, John, Ronald, Maureen, Anne, John Sandell, Barbara and myself. This was quite a party that went out of the Hospital gate that June morning.

When at last we were on our way, we had a police escort all the way to Newhaven. We seemed to go a different way from usual, but it was very grand to be out in the country at quite an early hour, and to feel that a wonderful holiday lay ahead.

We arrived at Newhaven at 10.30 am so we had plenty of time to get aboard the ship whose name was "The Londres". We did not see the Customs Officer at Newhaven, so as soon as we were taken from the coach and lifted straight onto the ship we were taken over to the starboard side and set against the rails and faced outward. Before we started our voyage across the channel, we had some sandwiches and something to drink. The boat set sail at 11.30 am and with only a gentle breeze, and a very smooth sea, the crossing was most pleasant.

The French tricolour was hoisted about ten minutes from the coast of France. We sighted land at about 2.10 pm, but we didn't arrive in Dieppe until 2.55 pm After we docked we went ashore, and waited on the quay for the Customs Officer but he only wanted to see our passports. When we had finished with the customs, we went to a little café around the corner called "The Celtic Bar". We just had something to eat and drink and then we started our one hundred miles, or 150 kilometres, journey to Garches, which is about the same distance from Paris as Carshalton is from London. The roads were a little rougher than the English ones, but except for an accident whilst crossing the Seine when a lorry with a piece of iron protruding from it buckled our rear left mudguard, we had a very good journey to Garches. We arrived at the Hospital Raymond Poincare' where we were to stay by 8.30 pm. This meant we had travelled for twelve hours! The first meal we had in France came in six courses – 1) Soup, 2) Meat with gravy, 3) Runner beans, 4) Potatoes, 5) Egg custard, 6) Fruit. Every course was served on a separate dish, so different from our English meal. We went to bed on a beautiful soft mattress at 10 pm.

The next day we visited Fontainebleau and the Chateau there. After we had toured most of the rooms, we had a break for a dejeuner, as the French call it, at a 'restaurant off the main road'. We had a very good meal, especially as we adopted the French custom of drinking wine and beer during the meal.

We had our money changed into francs that morning, but we kept getting mixed up with new and old francs.

In the afternoon we visited the Fontainebleau Forest and sat underneath the tree and wrote postcards to our friends.

That evening we went to the Hospital School Hall to see some dancing, but unfortunately the dancers did not turn up so a show was put on at short notice. The French children sang to us and then wanted us to sing to them, so we sang "Green grow the rushes, O". After that we gave a pianist four notes and he composed a tune in twist time, and then like Chopin. That ended a very happy second day in France.

The next few days were busy with visits to Versailles, Chantilly, the Eiffel Tower – from which we saw a wonderful view of Paris – and a tour on the right bank of the Seine. On Saturday we went for a tour of Paris by night, when we saw The Invalides, the Eiffel Tower, the Palais Royal, the Bastille, and then up the Champs Elysees to the Arc de Triomphe. All these were just a few of the famous places we saw. We even saw where the lights were among the trees, and followed them to the special statues or streets where the illuminations were.

Monday morning was a free one so some of us went to the Hospital shop, and some went to the Roman Catholic Church. For the afternoon, we went and visited the Vincennes Zoo in Paris. It was smaller than the London Zoo, but was set out so cleverly that you would not miss anything. The same evening we went and saw a modern ballet which was very good. It was in three parts and the last one, which was a modern variation of the Bolero, was the best.

The next day we went for a trip up the Seine in a boat called La Parisian. We started just past the Eiffel Tower, and steamed by the L'Ile de la Cite, back down the other side where we saw the statute of justice and then after this another interesting trip back we came to the landing stage. At supper that night we met the people who came to England. We were shown some photographs of their holiday. After lunch we were pushed to Garches town centre to buy anything that we forgot to buy at the Louvre stores where we went to do most of our shopping. On our way to Garches, we passed through a little village called Marnes-la-Coquette, where Louis Pasteur died, and nearby Maurice Chevalier lives.

All good things come to an end, so that evening we had a farewell party which was given in the High School. It started off with the Hospital Choir singing some French songs to us in parts. After that we heard the children play on descant recorders, and then a different group played the recorders in parts, which sounded very lovely.

Mrs Lawson translated a speech which I gave her into French, and I read it out to the people at the farewell party, thanking them for giving us such a lovely holiday. After we had said goodbye to everybody we went to bed.

We were up at 6.30 am the next morning so as to be ready to leave Garches at 8.30 am. After breakfast we started off and arrived in Dieppe at 12.15 pm.

We got on to the boat which was called 'The Arromanches' and left for Newhaven at 1.00 pm. The sea on this crossing had a slight swell, and just outside Newhaven we ran into a sea mist, so we went below deck. We docked at Newhaven at 4.30 pm. The Customs Officer only wanted to see the adults so we stayed in the boat until they came back and loaded us into the coach.

We left Newhaven at 5.00 pm and arrived back in Carshalton at 6.30 pm – ending the most wonderful holiday we have ever had!

By Gerald Thomas, Ward E10

MY VISIT TO HOLLAND

To be given the honour to travel and see some of the hospitals, rehabilitation centres and schools for handicapped children in the Netherlands was indeed a great privilege for me.

The receptions at these establishments were quite impressive and most welcoming, particularly at the Julianas Kinderziekenhuis. Everyone seemed so friendly and gave one the impression of one happy family. The tour has many very pleasant and happy memories which I shall never forget.

Several of the establishments were 'young'. Their Governing Bodies had spent much time in thought for planning and incorporating all modern methods and facilities with no thought of cost, an admirable feature I should say. There seems to have been no 'old buildings' incorporated into their schemes – hence the appearance was fresh, clean and neat.

There seemed to be no shortages of staff wherever I went and each person was included in 'Their Teams' – most essential in dealing with physical and mental illnesses and handicapped children.

The highlight of my visit was having the great honour of being presented to HRH Queen Juliana when she made an informal visit to Goois Kinderziekenhuis, an honour which I shall always cherish.

Much thanks is due to Baron Adolf Bentinck for arranging such a pleasant tour. May I take this opportunity of thanking everyone who gave me such a welcome in the Netherlands, but especially the Jewish Aid Committee for making the trip possible.

by Edith Ford

PROGRAMME

Monday June 25, 1962
between 9.30 and 10.30 am
Arrival at the Children's Hospital 'Juliana Kinderziehenhuis', nr.2, Dr van Welylaan, The Hague Tel: 39-23-00. Reception by Nurse Slingerland, Matron and Dr Van Zeben, Medical Superintendent.

Stay at the hospital from 25 June till 3 July inclusive. During that time there will be some excursions, a.o. Monday June 25 at 11.30 am excursion (together with nurses of the hospital) to the 'Mytyl School' at Rijswijk (near The Hague), school for spastic children.

Juliana Children's Hospital, Dr van Welylaan 2, The Hague
25 June – 1 July 1962

Monday June 25, 1962

11.30 am	Mytyl School, van Vredenburghweg, Rijswijk,	Miss Slingerland
3.00 pm	Interview Press	
4.00 pm	Tour round the Hospital	Miss Slingerland

Tuesday June 26, 1962

9.00 am – 12.30 pm	Infectious ward	Miss Remijnse
2.00 pm – 4.30 pm	Occupational therapy	Miss Blom

Wednesday June 27, 1962

7.45 am – 9.30 am	Out-patients department	Miss de Looy
9.30 am – 12.30 pm	Surgical ward	Miss Stap Miss Roos
2.30 pm – 5.30 pm	Sight seeing	Miss Schiphorst

Thursday June 28, 1962

9.00 am – 12.30 pm   Babies ward   Miss Dubbelman
                                                 Miss Engels

3.00 pm – 5.30 pm   Medical ward   Miss Verhagen

Friday June 29, 1962

8.30 am – 10.00 am   Out-patients department Dr van der Bas

10.00 am – 12.30 pm Medical ward   Miss Zephat

Weekend   Sight-seeing

Monday July 2, 1962

8.30 am   A car of the Ministry will call at the hospital in order to take you to Bussum

10.00 am   for a visit to the children's hospital at Bussum, called 'Goois Kinderziekenhuis'. Dr Steyling, Matron: Miss K Loostenhuis. At the end of the afternoon or day, return to The Hague by car.

Tuesday July 3, 1962

10.00 am   By train or car from the Ministry to Arnhem for a visit to the 'Johanna Stichting', a rehabilitation home for young children. Arriving by train you have to take bus nr.9 (direction Heyenoord) from the station Arnhem to the terminal. At the end of the afternoon or day, return by train or car to The Hague (hospital).

Wednesday July 4, 1962

approx.   A car of the Ministry will call at the hospital in order to
9.00 am   take you (with your luggage) to the 'Mr Dr Willem van den Bergh Stichting' (home for mentally deficient children), 2 Swarteweg, Noordwijk-Binnen.

10.00 am   Reception by the Medical Superintendent: Dr Chr. Steketee. Stay at this hospital from July 4 till 6 inclusive.

Why I desire to become a nurse

Before I left my native British Guiana a year ago, if anybody had suggested to me to make Nursing my career I would have simply laughed at him (or her) because at that time I couldn't reason with myself how a man can throw away his manhood (that's what I thought) and enter a profession that was dominated by women. Indeed, even though I had visited hospitals at home, I couldn't remember having seen a single male nurse.

So I came to England with no specific choice of profession in mind and secured a job as an accounts clerk. After the first few weeks it slowly dawned upon me that I was doing nothing useful. I was just earning money for my daily existence and (my reader will think me hypocritical) not contributing towards the welfare of Mankind. Besides, I wanted to be trained to do something that can be a valuable asset to me for the rest of my life and stand me in good stead for a job at home, should I return.

One day, acting on an impulse, I bought a "Nursing Mirror" and applied to the Fountain Hospital to be selected for Mental Training. I had also come to accept the fact that nursing was not only for women, and so in a few weeks I entered the lecture room of Queen Mary's for my first lecture.

I hope my gentle reader understands me. Sir, I am really eager, now more than ever to finish my training. Should I be successful, my ambition is to take a Tutor's Course as I would like to pass on to others what I've learnt. However, I feel that to be trained in Mental Handicap is not only a career but a privilege. A privilege to help and understand, instead of loathing, a person who, through no fault of his, is mentally unbalanced or deficient. I believe a training such as this will make me a tolerant, humane and understanding citizen, and equip me with a knowledge that will help me to help my fellow men who need my kind of help.

R.A.

The Fountain Hospital, Tooting, London and the transfer to Queen Mary's

Brenda Elliot

Pre-fabricated buildings were familiar to everyone in the post 1939-45 war period, but the pre-fabricated buildings at the Fountain Hospital, Tooting, dated from the very beginning of this century. They were intended to accommodate fever patients. The famous Edith Cavell spent a short time there as a student nurse. Later the Fountain became a Children's Hospital, caring for those with learning difficulties, many having to cope with the additional burden of physical disability. As a result of the social conditions existing at the time, it became a permanent home for all age groups. Despite major disadvantages, this situation produced a secure and stable environment, where residents grew up with the same companions, and often with the same staff, but with limited contact with the outside world.

In the mid 1950s' as a result of the nursing experience in a similar hospital overseas, I commenced a two year post-registration course at the Fountain, which would enable me to transfer to this special area of care, about which I, in company with most of the general public, knew very little.

The local administration was in the hands of a formidable team of Medical Consultants and Nursing staff, for the Ministry of Health was the responsible authority. Despite antiquated buildings, over crowding of patients and under-staffing - a programme of change was in operation. Ahead of the legislation, which would come later in the decade, there was more flexibility in the admissions policy, allowing children to come in for short-term care and assessment, and then to return to their homes. Training programmes for patients and staff were introduced. Already the unit for women at Streatham was providing simple training, enabling them to assist on the wards, in the laundry, needleroom and Hospital School. This was a traditional form of employment, but now a large house nearby was acquired as a Hostel, where the more able residents could live whilst experiencing suitable employment in the community. The final stage for a minority was independence through moving out to a bed-sit, with back-up from the hospital social worker.

Osborne House, a large house in extensive grounds at Orr, Hastings was a home to a group of older boys. Those who were able to go out to work were found jobs locally. The Ellen Terry Home at Reigate was a small unit for children with the additional handicap of blindness, or partial sight.

My two-year course encompassed experience in all but the last of these units, and I also had to spend a period of time in the Hospital School. My memories are of staff members who had known the residents for many years and who, in difficult conditions struggled to maintain a high standard of physical care, whilst being frustrated because the combination of over-crowding and under-staffing prevented them from giving individual attention where it was needed most.

In some wards all the children went to school. Three nurses would supervise the dressing, breakfasting and general preparation of their fifty children, and then accompany them to school. the school was staffed by teachers qualified to teach children with learning difficulties, many of them, including the Headmistress having first trained as nurses in this field. Some of the children attending were confined to wheel chairs, and the learning ability of the pupils covered a wide range, so that teaching them required much patience and understanding. The atmosphere was a very happy one and singing action-songs, dancing and percussion playing were part of the curriculum.

Just before Christmas a moving Nativity Play would be presented. The announcement that "I'm going to be Mary" or "I'm an Angel" often coming from the most unlikely Mary or Angel, but the casting was so often right on the day. In the summer the children had a Fête day - not a fund-raising public occasion, but a Fun Day when the teachers dressed all the pupils in fancy dress, and even the adults enjoyed joining in the fun. The parade was a long procession of familiar figures in unfamiliar clothes, weaving it's way through the hospital grounds. In December we would take parties to a preview of the Bertram Mills circus - the Matron remarked to me on one occasion that the clown's bicycle was similar to the one I rode to work! A visit to the Wimbledon Theatre pantomime was another regular part of the celebrations - often the plot was not easy to follow, but the splendour of the stage settings, the costumes and exciting lighting were all much appreciated.

The grounds of the hospital were not extensive, but a small Pet's Corner had been introduced, so that the children could see, and even handle some of the animals. I remember arriving one morning to see a small group of people watching one of the monkeys, sitting on the roof of a nearby Victorian terraced house, crouching against the warm chimney.

Summer holidays started in March and finished in October. Groups of twenty patients and four staff would be driven by the hospital coach to Osborne House at Hastings. here we stayed in two bungalow huts in the garden of the house. We were able to play in the grounds and organise coach outings - one to Camber Sands being very popular. Children and staff benefited from the relaxed atmosphere. A very active League of Friends, which included many parents, raised funds to provide "extras" on these social outings, and supported the hospital in its programme of change.

Just within the hospital gates stood a fountain in the form of a child bearing a tortoise on his back. At the completion of a nursing course, the successful student was presented with the hospital badge. It was a child holding a tortoise, representing the purpose of the training - to enable the candidate to assist the child to develop skills and lighten the burden of disability.

Throughout the time I was at the Fountain, any child needing special medical or surgical treatment was transferred to St. George's Hospital, which was in the process of taking over the Fever Hospital site across the road. Our children were so well cared for and fussed over in St. George's, and we were always able to visit and keep in touch.

After training I worked on a new unit, converted from part of the original ward, but with only twelve children. Now it was possible to give individual attention and create a more natural and homelike atmosphere. We watched our little family develop and change, an opportunity which would be given to all our children in a few years.

The need for new buildings was obvious, and a committee was formed, which included representatives form various disciplines concerned. As a result plans for a new hospital were prepared, and a new site at Tooting was allocated. Meanwhile, because of new advances in paediatrics, the bed occupancy at Queen Mary's Hospital for Children in Carshalton had been reduced. Children requiring an in-patient treatment were frequently admitted for a short period to busy adult medical or surgical wards. Fewer beds were required in the long stay wards where, in the past, children recovering from conditions such as rheumatic fever and poliomyelitis, had been nursed. Consequently in 1961 a Ministerial decision was made to combine the two hospitals on the Carshalton site - the new hospital as a result of the merger to operate as a Comprehensive Hospital for Children.

Prior to the merger there was a period of considerable unrest and anxiety. The Matron accepted a senior nursing post in Scotland, but most of the Assistant Matrons and Ward Sisters agreed to transfer to Carshalton, knowing that they would continue to be responsible for patients they already knew. Free transport was provided to ferry nursing and domestic staff between Tooting and Carshalton for a number of years.

The creation of a comprehensive Hospital affected everyone who contributed to the daily running of the hospital. The provision of nursing care being the responsibility of the most senior nurse a Group Matron's post was established, and the Matron of Q.M.H. was appointed. Her team of senior nursing staff, which included the tutors of both Nurse Training Schools tackled the challenging task of providing nursing care for all patients, and the statutory nurse training for students involved with nursing care in both sectors.

Meanwhile the children (those under sisters) were gradually transferred to Carshalton. They left behind the old wards which had been arranged on both sides of a long corridor. Each ward was quite wide and long, with a combined drying room and play room, separated from the dormitory area by a flimsy screen. The dormitory had four rows of beds or cots, and the whole area was heated by two parallel steam pipes beneath ornate metal gratings in the floor. From these gratings rose warm air, heavy with the aroma of dried dust and anything else spilt in the coarse of daily life on the ward. At Q.M.H. patients and staff were moved into up-graded wards, adapted for their needs, and with new equipment and furnishings. The day room was quite separate from the dormitory and there was ample space for twenty residents. Each ward had a play-ground and patients and their visitors were able to benefit from the spaciousness of their new surroundings. There was a Pets Corner, and later an indoor swimming pool. When special surgical or medical treatment was necessary, the child was able to be treated by transfer to a paediatric ward, instead of, as previously to another hospital.

Some time prior to the closing of The Fountain, the special

educational needs of all children with learning problems had become the responsibility of the Ministry of Education. New senior staff were appointed and all necessary changes made before The Fountain School moved to Carshalton, where it continued to be known as The Fountain School.

The advantageous conditions which existed at Carshalton, enabled our children to develop physically and emotionally. It was now possible to spend more time encouraging limited speech and manual dexterity, leading to greater independence. Having known their previous upper limits of accomplishment, parents and staff watched with joy this new development, which was a great encouragement to all concerned.

The old buildings of The Fountain were knocked down. The new St. George's Hospital was built on the large site where The Fountain, the Fever Hospital, and the road which once separated them, had been.

I am glad I trained at The Fountain when I did. I had a glimpse of the past - old buildings, old ways, old equipment, and even a few old ideas. But, at the same time, I saw how much could be achieved, even in poor surroundings, by sheer hard work, combined with deep concern on the part of the carers. Fortunately I also saw the transformation which occurred as a result of improving the physical environment. The result only came about because of the continuing devotion, informed loving care and patience of all involved in caring for those who have a learning disability.

The Fountain School
Queen Mary's Hospital for Children

Having moved back to Surrey, my most recent home, in 1971 I found time on my hand and offered to take part in voluntary work at QM Hospital.

My three children had started at school and I had time to spare.I contacted the hospital matron, who, learning that I was a school teacher, suggested that I might be useful in one of the two hospital schools.

She took me first to visit the hospital school for those having treatment and who were staying for varying lengths of time.

Sadly, that school was closed for holiday time. Matron then took me to see the Fountain School which had been built with money kindly donated by The Worshipful Company of Drapers.

I had been almost totally unaware that children with severe learning difficulties were housed at Queen Mary's. Many of them lived permanently on the hospital wards but some of the less severely handicapped were given rooms, during week days, in the Fountain School.

I thought that there must be many people in the world who were totally unaware of the numerous children and adults who appeared to live in such a small world of their own.

I was told by the head teacher that the Local Education Authority in Carshalton would be interviewing teachers who might be interested in working with special needs children and in learning about them and their differing disabilities.

Some children – very few – attended the school on a daily basis but most of them lived on wards, in the day room, or in twenty bedded rooms at that time.

I was invited to attend an interview and, to my amazement, was invited to take a part-time job since my own children came out of school early and needed me to meet them. I accepted. What had I let myself in for! I was a worried woman!!

I had anticipated some introduction to the correct ways of helping the children but – on my first day – had to take over a small class of the most disruptive children as their teacher was very ill! Needless to say, I was very worried of course!

Boxes of bricks, toys, paper and games were actively hurled across the room and I had been given no idea of how to control them and no help. Their usual teacher was obviously the expert and I was not! It was a blessing to see her when she returned.

I was later introduced to a lovely classroom for the most physically disabled children. None could speak but most understood what we said or signed. They loved to be on the floor, out of their wheelchairs where we painted, rolled, sang, clapped and moved to music. We had ample visual aids and toys and games there. Their faces showed their happiness. We walked with wheel chairs around the grounds. To be recognised and smiled at gave great rewards to my lovely classroom helper, Anne, who loved the group as much as I.

There were many children at the hospital who had no education at the time I was there. I was asked if I would be the first teacher on the wards for the children with severe learning difficulties. I was very sad to leave my little disabled group but was pleased to help the babies on Ward C1 and then those on C2, C4, C6, F7 and F8. We were able to help a little, I think.

I bought toys as there were so few on the wards at the time. Rattles, singing drums etc., were much appreciated.

As my children were growing older I was able to work over the lunch time and give more help. We were able to take the children out into the grounds more often, but I had no helper then.

The experience gained at Queen Mary's was great and I shall always be grateful for my introduction to the Fountain School where I learned so much. From working with my physically disabled children at the Fountain School, I knew that I wanted to work more with physically disabled children who might well also have learning difficulties.

I applied to the headmaster at St Margaret's School, Croydon, and was accepted there. I worked for two groups, for Croydon, Sutton & District Spastics Society and, for a short while, at the Shaftesbury Society.

I shall always be grateful for what I have experienced and learned at Queen Mary's Hospital and for the building of the Fountain School and those who provided it and mostly for the friends I made there, young and old.

The Fountain School was a wooden one-storey building (slightly devoid of fresh air owing to the positioning of the toilets!) which provided rooms for the Muscular Dystrophy boys to enjoy arts and crafts and to give staff space to work.

Thank you to you all.

I am delighted that my oldest daughter has never wanted to work anywhere but at Queen Mary's Hospital since she was a tiny girl. She still works there – is nearly 40 and has just set up a new home inside the gates of the hospital for older folk with learning difficulties. Her grandfather – my father – worked on the management committee years ago. Three generations, of which I am proud to be one!

Sylvia Stronge

Ernest and
Frances Earl
with Red Rum

TREES

Of all the creation in the world
the loveliest of all are trees.
The proud beauty of a lonely pine,
the rugged splendour of a solitary oak,
The whispering magic of a forest deep;
these put a troubled mind at ease.
I think of an oak grown tall and stately,
or a silver birch exquisite and tiny.
Each a true expression of life pure and humble,
lonely and yet divinely proud.
Each one rising and putting out branches,
growing more lovely,
Growing like angels thoughts transcendent,
nearer and nearer to God

Frances Earl (née Lloyd)
Written at the age of 11 years
A former member of the hospital school staff

A Sculptor's Vision of Education
– from the Fine Group by Albert Toft

First Steps
– A sculpture by Mademoiselle Bricard

LONDON BOROUGH OF SUTTON

Chief Education Officer, H. M. Evans, MA(Oxon.)

EDUCATION DEPARTMENT
The Grove, Carshalton, Surrey tel. 01-647 5501 ext

Your ref
My ref   SD/TS

date   **10 MAY 1972**

Dear Sir/~~Madam~~,

_____Fountain_____School

    With reference to my letter of ————— regarding
your temporary appointment as a teacher in the above school
from 8ᵗʰ May 1972 , I have to advise
you that your salary has been provisionally assessed, pending
receipt of your Teachers Service Card from the Department of
Education and Science and/or verification of your status and service
at the rate of £ 1808.00 per annum including London Allowance.

    You will be advised as soon as possible if any variation in
your salary becomes necessary.

                Yours faithfully,

                H.M. EVANS

                Chief Education Officer

Mr E. A. Earl,
6, Dundrey Crescent,
Merstham,
Surrey

All correspondence to be addressed to the Chief Education Officer.

My appointment to the Fountain School staff, 8th May 1972

SOME SUGGESTIONS TO AID IN THE TEACHING OF MENTALLY HANDICAPPED CHILDREN

"The counsel thou wouldst have another keep just keep it thyself."

The following article I produced shortly after starting as a teacher in the Fountain School. I reprint it here in order that it may give an insight into the work of the teacher.

Some extracts from a talk by Dr M Kellmer-Pringle, Director, National Children's Bureau at the Conference on Co-operation in Care and Education, Bournemouth April 19-21 1972.

Co-operation in Residential Child Care
The aims of co-operation were to enable children to achieve their emotional social and intellectual potential. There was no way of knowing precisely what that potential was but it was known that fruitful interaction with the environment was a prerequisite.

The basic needs of handicapped children are the same as those of normal children. The first of these is security, which is essential to learning and depends upon the quality of a human relationship. The second is a need for new experiences, which are essential to growth; many handicapped children are environmentally deprived. A third need is for recognition of achievement; usually children who need praise most tend to get least. Lastly, children need to achieve some measure of personal independence; for example ability to wash and dress and to take responsibility of a personal possession.

Play can help to satisfy basic needs. All treatment plans should be concerned with progressive objectives and not be restrictive. Teachers' expectations influence the performance of children.

Where parents are not available, the child has a need for a continuous and dependable relationship with one or two adults. The vast majority of mentally handicapped children have some potential for learning and all persons who come into contact with them have the responsibility for stimulating it.

In the discussion which followed the talk it was asked if it were not possible to over-estimate some mentally handicapped children. There was little evidence, Dr Kellmer-Pringle thought, to suggest that over-stimulation was damaging but there should be a treatment plan and sensitive observation of the effects of the environment on children, for children show progress in different areas at different times. The treatment plan must take note of the whole child, flexibility must be a feature of it; re-assessment and the recognition of learning plateaux were essential.

ESSENTIALS FOR EDUCATIONAL DEVELOPMENT

1. To be considered as children, not types or cases.
2. To have freedom of movement and activities in a specially structured environment.
3. To receive continued praise and approval.
4. To have an immediate response to natural interests and to language.
5. To have opportunities for play which is understood by the teacher.
6. To have a special kind of teacher.
7. To have a varied and stimulating programme of activities.
8. To have planned systematic individual teaching by the same teacher over a long period of time.

THE VALUE OF TEACHING THROUGH PLAY

"A child who has never learned to play properly will continually meet with difficulties in his later development." – K & C Buhler.

In an effective teaching programme it is important that the children are taught, frequently and consistently, in a play situation so that the children are involved emotionally rather than intellectually in working towards a specific goal. The specific goal which is the broadening of their experience and development of potential can be achieved if they are given purposely designed games which help to increase:

Verbal Communication	Visual Perception
Memory	Understanding of Numbers
Colour, Shape, Size discrimination	Alertness
Speed of Response	Hand/Eye co-ordination
Social Awareness	

Games which help towards attaining this goal are those which could involve a form of competition, as for example in snap where the children have to turn over two cards with the same number, picture, shape or colour on them.

Handicapped children need to have social experiences in play activities as do all other children. This may take the form of solitary play, spectator play, parallel play, associative play and group play. This will aid social and emotional development. The more opportunities the children have for play which is developed by the teacher, the more likely it is that language will be developed in both increased comprehension and expression.

Solitary play is the only possible form of play for the very youngest children. Later, solitary play implies the will to be independent and alone with the material available to others, too. No attempt to associate with others appears during play. Looking on play may mean verbal contact or only watching what others do. Parallel play means that all the children use the same playthings but play side by side rather than with each other.

One feature of associative play is that children take ideas from each other, borrow and lend toys or tools. They may also supervise each other's actions, but follow their own inclinations. The object of the play or work is outside the actual group interest.

In co-operative play, on the other hand, the object is to achieve a certain result together and the task is organised with this end in view. The term implies conscious co-operation between the members of the group.

In 'activity method' teaching, strong emphasis is laid on co-operation and endeavours are made to construct tasks suitable for joint activities, for they are of the utmost importance in fostering better social co-operation.

C. I. Sandstrom

Just like normal children, handicapped children show others their knowledge and observation of the world around them. The teacher can use play as a vehicle for introducing relevant language at the moment when it is most understood.

As the children get older, they need to have opportunities to repeat the initiative and representational play of a younger chronological age which is usually carried out without language. If the language response from the teacher has been developed over the years, then they can develop their play at a more sophisticated level, that is, accompanied by language.

Child psychologists, such as Piaget, see play as an important aspect of intellectual development. Children learn to concentrate during play activities; they become absorbed.

Teachers of handicapped children are largely concerned with that stage of development, the sensory motor period (interplay of movement and perception) during which period play starts. When the child's behaviour goes beyond the reflex stage new elements become embodied in the circular reaction between stimuli and responses but the child's activities are still only a repetition of what he has done before. Piaget calls the 'reproductive assimilation' doing what was done before when such actions are well within the child's capacity. Such repetition 'for its own sake' is the forerunner of play.

It is not until the child is between 12-18 months old that there is active systematic experimentation. In the final stage of the sensory-motor period action in the absence of objects and with it symbolisation pretence and make-believe become possible. Symbolic or make-believe play characterises the period of representational intelligence from about 2-7 years of age.

Initially, thinking takes the form of substitute actions which still belong to the last of the sensory-motor developments. Actions appropriate to one object are used as a substitute. Initially these interiorised actions stand for the object, as concrete symbols – later they act as signs indicating or signifying the object. Language is a socially ready-made set of signifiers – words which held the process but are not essential to it.

Symbolic and make-believe play has the same function in the development of representational play as practical play had in the sensory motor period. It is pure assimilation and consequently repeats and organises thinking in terms of images and symbols already mastered. Symbolic play also functions to assimilate and consolidate the child's emotional experiences. During the representative period, make-believe play becomes progressively more elaborate and organised.

With growing experience of the physical and social environment, there is a transition to more accurate representation of reality. This increasingly involves sensory-motor and intellectual practice so that play becomes constructive, adapted to reality and ceased to be play altogether. At the same time, the child becomes more socially adapted and consequently needs to resort less to symbolic substitutes and distortions of reality.

From the practical implications of these theories it appears that the mental processes of the child will be stunted if he is not given the fullest opportunity to express himself in play. Play involves learning and giving selected response to stimulation.

PHYSICAL DEVELOPMENT

"No amount of practice can make a child sit, walk, talk or acquire other skills until his nervous system is ready for it. On the other hand, delay in the acquisition of skills may be caused by depriving the child of opportunity to practice them when sufficient maturation has occurred." (Illingworth 1966, p77)

It is hoped that the children, by using the apparatus provided, such as the Southampton Cave climbing frame, and by taking part in games, will develop well co-ordinated movements and mobilise large joints. Traditional exercises such as arm raising are also valuable as well as simple indoor games such as rolling a ball at skittles, which are helpful in developing hand/eye co-ordination.

In the adventure playground, activities such as climbing, balancing on the catwalk, running and jumping, kicking and throwing a ball can take place. Though it is difficult to visualise that the children will play a team game in the normal context of the word, it is hoped that they might achieve a standard whereby they kick or throw a ball to each other.

Swimming is an important part of the physical education programme. Here, those children with a physical handicap can be encouraged to walk and exercise. Children find great enjoyment in swimming and it is hoped that this experience will make the activity self-reinforcing in that the children will want to go again – thus aiding emotional and physical development.

Another form of exercise is the Margaret Morris Movement, a method of physical education and creative dance combining therapeutic and aesthetic values. Exercises are devised with a physiological aim together with free movement and composition to draw out and develop the potentialities of each child.

Through all these forms of exercise, better posture and improvements in walking action should result, as well as better and improved all round co-ordinated movements.

DEVELOPING ENVIRONMENT

The classroom environment should develop as the children's interests emerge and as the teacher begins to understand their needs. The environment should be dynamic not static. Arrangement of the room and the pictorial work of the teacher and children should be changed from time to time for novelty is an important feature of learning. Sameness may bring about boredom and lack of interest and concentration. The appearance of the classroom indicates the way in which the work is based and how new experiences are being introduced enabling the children to build up concepts. It also indicates how the children are being helped to relive their experiences planned by the teacher, through representation of all kinds.

REASONS FOR INDIVIDUAL WORK

1. The attention factor. The teacher is more liable to secure the child's attention over a longer period of time on tasks that he wants him to do rather than if group methods are used. Also the child is more liable to concentrate.

2. The teacher is more likely to adjust his language to a particular child if he is with him in a one-to-one relationship. In learning, language skills the child has to learn to imitate the movement of the adult's lips and mouth used in the formation of words. The handicapped child is more likely to do this if he is near enough to his teacher's face for his facial expressions and lip movements to cause an impact on his awareness.

3. Wide discrepancies in ability. In any one administrative group it is highly likely that each child is at a different level of achievement in a variety of learning areas. It is therefore impossible for the teacher to approach the learning difficulties in any structural way unless it is with individual children.

4. Developing the teacher's skills. All children are responsible for their teacher's learning and professional development. In working with handicapped children this is also true. What he learns from his time spent with individual children will flow into his work with the group and help him to become more efficient. Teaching aids he devises for individual children he will be able to use with other children and with a group.

5. Confusion might result if the teacher is not consistent in handling materials. Particularly if the teacher wants the child to construct the thing in the same way as he has done. Also if too many instructions are given at any one time.

AIMS FOR HANDICAPPED CHILDREN
It is hoped that some of the children will go on to live in hostels or half-way houses. If this is the case it is important that they be helped to function at a higher level, be less dependent and more socially aware. To meet these requirements the programme is organised so that it tackles:-

Language Development	Writing
Money Dealing	Road Drill
Shopping	Cooking
Cleaning	Hygiene
Social Behaviour	Group Awareness

BEHAVIOUR OF THE TEACHER IN THE CLASSROOM
Some quotations from the book by Gardener and Cass. Quotations come from the section headed 'Actions of the Teacher which show concern with promoting social attitudes by direct example'.

Requests the child's help or co-operation
Enlists co-operation between the child and himself
Promotes social attitudes between children or considerate behaviour
Arbitrates
Provides an audience that other children shall watch
Thanks a child
Asks a child's permission
Asserts by word or gestures

Praises child's performance, work or action
Stimulates by encouragement
Helps by doing part of a child's work for him
Praises a child's gift, possessions, help or appearance

To achieve the above qualities means that the teacher has to be continuously aware of his own active role in the learning situation. There is no place for the attitude of letting the children 'get on by themselves'.

SOME TEACHING RULES

1. Always start from something within the child's experience and move gradually towards the unknown.

2. Introduce the 'thing' first, then the 'name' and then the 'sign'.

3. Make all speech as graphic as possible, that is by illustrating words with drawings and paintings etc. Less able children cannot think in the abstract.

4. There are different levels of concept awareness. A child will only be aware of the concept within the context of his own experience. He cannot transfer knowledge easily. The aim is first to extend the experience and then normalising the experience to develop the concept. This requires frequent dialogue between teacher and child.

5. Always treat the child's work, especially any conversation, with respect. This is the main clue as to how their minds are working and should influence the teacher's next move.

6. Help the child to organise all work properly whatever the quality, for example, the making of a nature scrapbook. Be consistent with the standard that you accept.

7. Be consistent with rewards.

8. The child must achieve frequent success.

The aim in teaching is an attempt to marry the best of an informal approach to education to a systematic structured approach to the individual child.

The first approach takes into account the creative, social and emotional development of the child. The second is designed so that each child reaches maximum intellectual development relative to the handicap.

E A Earl
Fountain School
Queen Mary's Hospital for Children
Carshalton

References

(1) Mildred Stevens – The Educational Needs of Severely Handicapped Children

(2) C. I. Sandstrom – The Psychology of Childhood Adolescence

(3) Susanna Millar – The Psychology of Play

(4) William van der Eyken – The Pre School Years

(5) Senior Psychologist, St Lawrence's Hospital – Aims Through Play and Games Suggestions

(6) P Oakley, Teacher Remedial Department, Thomas Bennett Comprehensive School, Crawley, Sussex

(7) Celia M Smithson, Teacher, St Lawrence's Hospital School for Mentally Handicapped Children

Education Action 1993

Definition of special needs
A child has special educational needs if he or she has a learning difficulty which calls for special educational provision to be made for him or her.

A child has a learning difficulty if he or she:

a) has a significantly greater difficulty in learning than the majority of children of the same age;

b) has a disability which either prevents or hinders the child from making use of educational facilities of a kind provided for children of the same age in schools within the area of the local educational authority;

c) is under five and falls within the definition at a) or b) above, or would do if special educational provision was not made for the child.

A child must not be regarded as having a learning difficulty solely because the language or form of language of the home is different from the language in which he or she is or will be taught.

Special educational provision means:

a) for a child over two, educational provision which is additional to, or otherwise different from, the educational provision made generally for children of the child's age in maintained schools, other than special schools, in the area;

b) for a child under two, educational provision of any kind.

A child is a person who is under the age of nineteen and is a registered pupil at a school.

The 5-stage model of assessment and provision

Stage 1: Class or subject teachers identify or register a child's special educational needs and, consulting the school's SEN co-ordinator, take initial action;

Stage 2: The school's SEN co-ordinator takes lead responsibility for gathering information and for co-ordinating the child's special educational provision, working with the child's teachers;

Stage 3: Teachers and the SEN co-ordinator are supported by specialists from outside the school;

Stage 4: The LEA consider the need for a statutory assessment and, if appropriate, make a multidisciplinary assessment;

Stage 5: The LEA consider the need for a statement of special educational needs and, if appropriate, make a statement and arrange, monitor and review provision.

Warnock report says that 20% of children at some time have a special need.

Principles of the Code of Practice says:
- special educational needs must be addressed
- recognition of a continuum of needs and provision
- greatest possible access to a broad and balanced education
- most children with SEN needs will be in mainstream with no statement; many children with statement will be in mainstream
- action in the early years; LEA and the Health and Social Services
- partnership between parents and their children, schools, LEA's and other agencies.

SEN – A Guide for Parents

Some suggestions – Also ask to see the school's SEN policy!

1. Get in touch with the Local Educational Authority (LEA).

2. Ask the Head Teacher of a child's school to convene a meeting.

3. Invite parent, LEA representative, Class Teacher, and where possible, representatives of Health Services, Social Services or any other closely involved professional.

4. * PARENT of child put together any available evidence that may support case (* your views, knowledge, experience, etc.)

5. i)   Make sure that a meeting summarises outcomes and responds to child's needs and a further review meeting is set.
    ii) That School sets educational targets.
    iii) That this information will be circulated to all concerned who work with and support the child.
    iv) Get an effective assessment of child and a promise of provision to suit.

Extra Information

The school should familiarise themselves with the Acts of Parliament that directly affects the future provision available to a young person of Special Needs e.g. Child Act 1989 / NHS and Community Care Act 1990.

* Parent – What is your child like now? (Give relevant advice)

1. Child's general health
2. Physical skills
3. Self help – level of independence
4. Communication
5. Playing/learning at home. What does child do with his time? – hobbies?
6. Outside activities – clubs?
7. Relationships – family/friends, social?
8. Behaviour – co-operates, moods, demonstrative?
9. At school – relationships, children, teacher's progress reading/ writing/literacy/numeracy. Do you help with homework? What results?
10. Does child enjoy school?
11. What does he find easy or difficult?

Parents' General Views
1. What do you think your child's Special Educational needs are?
2. How do you think these can best be provided for?
3. How do you compare your child with others of the same age?
4. What is your child good at, or what does he enjoy doing?
5. What does he worry about? Is he aware of his difficulties?
6. What are your worries, concerns?
7. Is there any other information you would like to give?
   a) about family e.g. major events that might have affected your child
   b) reports from other people?
8. With whom would you like more contact?
9. How do you think your child's needs affect the needs of the family as a whole?

Queen Mary's and The Iron Age

Ronald Michell – Former Deputy Head, Hospital School

In one of the alcoves of the excellent little museum run by the Surrey Archaeological Society in Guildford, stands a glass showcase. Behind the glass are three large, smoke-blackened earthenware pots. A card beneath them is inscribed: Early Iron Age. Found at Queen Mary's Hospital, Carshalton.

I was on holiday when I first saw these grimy, misshapen objects, and had little wish to be reminded of Queen Mary's, but the contents of that case were a challenge that could hardly be ignored. What on earth was the Iron Age doing at Queen Mary's? Let me say in parenthesis that though I had suspected the existence of several old battle-axes at the Hospital, I should never have dreamed of looking for old pots there; but I was younger then, and have since probably qualified to join the old battle-axes myself. What was the Iron Age anyway? Could it have any connection with the woad-stained Ancient Britons of my schooldays? I had to find out.

"In 1908," says the Victoria History of Surrey, "workmen employed by the Metropolitan Asylums Board in building their new hospital uncovered the remains of a large Early British Settlement on Stag Hill near Carshalton." (Stag Hill? Hospitals East and West to you.) "The site showed signs of habitation during the Late Bronze and Early Iron Ages." So there it was! In the very place where troops of nurses wend their giggling way from the lecture rooms, once stood the mean huts of hairy Ancient Britons!

Take your stand on the remnants of Stag Hill (it is almost cut away by the sites of Hospitals East and West), look down the Main Drive and realise what an excellent look-out point it was. To your right and left, in pre-historic times, the chalk downs made an easy natural highway. There were probably fewer trees then than now, forest trees do not grow well on chalky soil, and the cattle of our villagers cleared the scrub more quickly than a team of modern gardeners do. Behind us, the downs rise towards Woodmansterne and Banstead upon whose breezy heights the Ordinance Survey map marks several burial mounds. Perhaps they were the tombs of the first "Queen Mary's" Chieftains. In front, the ground falls away in a gentle slope towards the Thames, ground then covered by dense, trackless forest, the home of the lean wolf, the evil tusked boar, and the terrible wild ox. To keep out such unwelcome visitors the village was surrounded by a ditch and palisade.

Other enemies were to be feared by these first residents of our grounds, for the country was in the process of colonisation by new, fair-haired invaders swinging long iron swords. These were the Celts, the men whose rumbling chariots chased the great Julius Caesar from our shores. It was some time during this period, according to the archaeologists, that the village on Stag Hill ceased to be occupied.

Were the inhabitants driven off to slavery by the Celts, or were they perhaps mown down by Caesar's Iron Legions? Or did they, in more settled times, move from their camp on the hill, which must have presented considerable problems of water supply, down to the edge of the Great Forest where springs of sweet water bubble into Carshalton ponds? We cannot know. The only testimony left to us now is a paragraph in the Victoria History and three blackened, cracked, cooking-pots standing in the showcase in an alcove of Guildford Museum.

Queen Mary's Hospital School

7/7/56

Dear Miss Shearn,

If I <u>can</u> be of any help in your project I shall be very pleased but I'm afraid I haven't any important information. All I know of the early years is of course hearsay. I'll tell you what I think are the facts and only hope they are correct. I expect dates could be verified at the office.

The hospital opened, I understand in 1910. John Burns, the politician, on a country bicycle ride (through the lavender fields of Carshalton!) saw the empty buildings which had been built for use as a fever hospital but never used. He climbed over the wall to explore and later suggested to the Metropolitan Asylums Board it would be a good spot for a children's hospital.

When opened all the patients had some form of tuberculosis. Years later the pulmonary cases were moved to Brentwood and some time in the 1920s it became a general hospital for cases needing long treatment e.g. osteomipelitis which before modern treatment took much longer to cure. In the late 1920s we began to receive many unfortunate paralysis patients and I should think in the early 1930s or even late 1920s the open air swimming pool was installed for hydrotherapy, the earliest in the British Isles and possibly in the world, though there is doubt about an Australian one having priority.

In the period shortly before 1920, Dr. Pugh the medical superintendent made surgical history with his invention, the carriages and with his enthusiasm for complete open-air treatment. He and Dr. Rollier of Leyson, Switzerland exchanged views and equipment including the carriages.

About 1932 the Metropolitan Asylums Board was, I think, disbanded. In any case at that time the London Country Council took over the hospital. The funds the Metropolitan Asylums Board had in hand were used to build the nurses' home and chapel.

Somewhere about the middle 1930s Sister Kenny was making a stir in Australia with her views on treatment for polio. She approached the L.C.C. who offered to give her full freedom to prove the value of her treatment for 2 years and chose Queen Mary's for the test. B7 and 8 (or A7 and 8) had a good deal of plumbing alterations under her directions. Miss Reardon worked with her and could tell you much more than I can. Miss Kenny later went to America to open clinics there and when our senior therapist (Miss Lindsay) returned she joined her there. I rather think the present polio treatment is a development but daren't be too dogmatic about that.

In the 1930's too the L.C.C. medical department set aside £30,000 (?) for research into child rheumatism and again Queen Mary's was chosen. E9and 10 and D9 and 10 were built and Dr. Gray and Hill with a research worker and visiting specialist carried out tests and made numerous records which, of course, I know nothing about.

About 1938 or 9 (it may have been a little later, 1942 possibly) the spastic patients were gathered to one ward and Mrs Collis who had been studying the treatment of cerebral palsy under Dr. Phelps in America was appointed to organise treatment. You know the development of that, of course, and how later, a succession of teachers attended the training courses Mrs Collis held for therapists so that treatment with education could mutually help each other.

Are the earliest school logs still in existence? If so, you must have had a few smiles. Do you notice how the head reported on her teachers and giving them marks?

I don't know when school first made its appearance. It was probably about 1912 - 14 for the Head I worked with first (Mrs Vallance) was appointed about 1918. There had been about three before, for short periods. I'm not surprised they did not stay, for conditions were, by all accounts, appalling.

Each teacher (there were three) had a block under her care, generally 64 children. They had half time school i.e. the teachers would be responsible for them from 9 - 10.30 while the nurses did treatment, washing etc. with the other half and changed over at 10.30 until 12, similarly in the afternoon 1.30 - 2.30 and 2.30 - 4. In addition children were of very mixed ages. By all accounts many hours were spent in copying long extracts from books, methods years out of date in schools even by then. By degrees more teachers were appointed until two were allocated to each flat i.e. one for each ward. In those days wards were always full and a teacher would have 16 in the ward 9 - 10.30 and 16 in the court yard 10.30 to 12 but in summer when all were outside the half not "in school" were often a bit of a nuisance.

As more teachers were appointed, the abundant children were

brought by attendants to school where there were two classes in the hall and one in each, now, staff room. Our staff room then was a ward day-room in F street.

One of our biggest changes in the educational method happened about 1926 or 7. Although gradually improving, the age grading on the wards was not as satisfactory as we wished, though Mrs Vallance was little by little gaining more respect for school and its needs from the medical side using her method of "peaceful penetration". But as patients often stayed from 3 to 8 years she was very concerned that in a ward with such varying ages and previous schooling and needs that education should be really systematic and thorough. So she devised an adapted form of the Walton plan where each could work at his own speed, systematically and, most important, would know how to read for content and arrange and express it and to think for themselves. Several committees of teachers met to help to devise the plan. It was revised from time to time and brought up to date but later as books got out of date we were unable to renew because of war conditions. In any case your conditions and needs are quite different now aren't they?

Funnily enough about the period Mrs Vallance was considering individual methods, I was driven to them in another way. I got landed with a class at school of 30 non-readers from all along C street, some of them boys of 15, well innoculated against learning anything! I got Mrs Vs permission to experiment on individual auto-education lines.

I dare not let the older boys know what low classes they were graded and so introduced a colour for each grade. The novelty of the approach made them sit up and take notice and though there were no miracles I got a few successes. I'm rather glad just to mention this for there was such an emasculated version of all this left behind that I knew you must have received a very queer impression. In 1940 London University officially recognised Queen Mary's as an examination centre for School Certificate with several successes.

During the time I have known Queen Mary's there have been various enthusiasms and vogues which after a while have passed to give way to others. I think this is quite a healthy sign and in any case is inevitable as teachers with their varying "gifts" come and go. Sometimes drama and puppeting have flourished. We had an excursion into pipe making years ago, but having no one of the calibre of Miss Bower it faded out. We've had two attempts at bee-keeping, the second ending with bombing and evacuation. For several years we had a very successful tuck-shop, the profits being used for outings (Zoo, British Museum, black-berrying by coach!) The tuck-shop arose because the long staying patients had such queer ideas of the value of money. (I was once asked to spend 6d. for a small boy and buy "a bag-full of chocolates, a bag-full of sponge cakes and spend the rest in stamps"!) Our tuck-shop profits came from sweets but we also sold stamps, stamp albums, fret work tools and wood, knitting needles and wools, needlework materials, games etc.

I expect most of this won't be any good to you at all. But if you are not too bored to read it all, you <u>may</u> get an overall picture from which to build your own. Your conditions are so vastly different today!

I don't know whether any of my snaps are of any use to you. Will it be early enough if I bring what I have to the Music Festival? Then we could have a little private session and you could have any you thought might be useful.

With all good wishes
Yours sincerely
Frances Linsey

P.S. By the way, the reason we gave up half-time school was when the L.C.C. wished, naturally, that the hospital should receive an education grant the Board stipulated for a minimum of two hours each session. Matron insisted on a late start - 9.30 - if she was to keep her bargain (no domestic work or washing during school time. Mrs V. insisted on this). The then superintendent didn't like teachers beginning at 9.30 (!) and in his turn insisted that teachers should still come at 9. So they came for preparation, library changing, and in a rota helped me with registration, stock etc. We, of course, had no secretary.

On the 6th May, 1912, three years after the official opening of the Children's Infirmary, two new members of staff commenced duty. These were the first teachers. The school was then directly under the control of the hospital (which was administered by the Metropolitan Asylums Board). The Medical Superintendent exercised considerable authority in the running of the school, and all requisitions for apparatus and material were submitted to him.

In 1930, the Metropolitan Asylums Board was disbanded and the London County Council became the controlling authority. The next year, after careful negotiations with the hospital staff, enabling all children to receive a minimum of two hours' education both morning and afternoon, the school was officially recognised as a Special School and qualified for a Board of education grant.

When, in 1948, the South West Metropolitan Hospital Board became the controlling authority for the hospital, the authority for the school was changed again, this time to the Surrey County Council.

Now, on April 1st, 1964, with the reorganisation of local government, Carshalton ceases to be in the administrative county of Surrey, and so responsibility for the education of the children in the hospital passes to the London Borough of Sutton.

Theses changes bring a measure of sadness to the staff who have worked for a particular authority for a long time, and a degree of anxiety with regard to the future. Yet the school history, recorded daily in the School Log Book, shows growth and development throughout the years, despite all the changes in administration, and despite, also, the changing nature of the hospital. The transfer to the L.C.C. promoted new growth.

Thanks to the support we have received from the Surrey County Council, and the sympathetic understanding of the School Governors, the school has been equipped and staffed in recent years for a greater range of work than ever before. For those who think in terms of numbers the school was at its zenith when it had six hundred children on the roll and a staff of fifty. But for those who think in terms of "special education," that is, education for the handicapped, the challenge of today's work is as vital as it has ever been. The importance of educational provision for the under fives, (which, for the uninitiated, means skilled direction of their play activities) for the very severely disabled, for the emotionally unstable, is recognised by the professions and administrative authorities and by the general public. Therefore, although we feel a little sad, we have every reason to look forward with confidence to further growth, as we develop a closer link than has been possible before with the neighbourhood in which we are situated.

"A Christmas Carol"
Annual School Party 1954
Miss Taylor, Mrs Cullis, pupil, Mr Hilditch, pupil, Miss Sprake

Teacher's play for Christmas Party 1955

*Christmas Party
1955*

*The teachers in
their play
costumes help
to serve tea*

*Children's Tableau
1959*

*for the school
carol service*

*Part of Children's Tableau
for 1960 Carol Service*

Happy times at Christmas

Achievement Against the Odds

From A Correspondent

Schoolmaster, May 18, 1962

Last Saturday the Queen Mary's Hospital School, Carshalton, the largest of its kind in the country, celebrated its 50th anniversary with an exhibition of children's work.

At first sight, the work closely resembled that done in any other school. There were gay items of pottery and woodwork, colourful textiles, numerous paintings, drawings, models and cookery samples.

Yet many of the exhibits were the product of a long, painful and heroic struggle with physical disability.

One boy, both arms paralysed by polio, had painted some remarkable pictures, lying flat on his back, with a paper board suspended over his head, and clasping his brush between his teeth. A girl, suffering from cerebral palsy, and with very little control over her muscles, had taken hours to assemble radio parts which normal children would have accomplished in a few minutes.

The teaching conditions in the hospital present enormous difficulties to the staff. The wards are organised according to ailments, not ages, so in a typical ward there is a range from two to sixteen. The teachers too have constantly overcome the physical disabilities of the children.

Holes and slots

In the domestic science room, for instance, there were tables with holes and slots into which mixing bowls and basin could be set to enable children with the use of only one hand to be able to mix ingredients without having simultaneously to grasp the side of the bowl to steady it.

On the other hand, the school enjoys an abnormally high teacher to pupil ratio - some thirty teachers for two hundred pupils. But quite apart from physical difficulties, the children require an unusual degree of individual attention. Without the stimulus of competition which they would normally gain from class work, they need a great deal of encouragement from their teachers.

232

Some of the most important and rewarding work is done with children suffering from muscular dystrophy, whose condition is progressively deteriorating and who have no hope of recovery. For them school work is the only outlet they possess, and without it they would rapidly decline into a condition of apathy.

One encouraging aspect is the progressive decline in the number of children with chronic or incurable illnesses. At one time they constituted a majority of pupils, but with medical advances which have led to the virtual elimination of tubercular and polio cases, the proportion is now down to 25 per cent.

The exhibition, which brought great joy to the children, their parents and the medical staff at the hospital, reflected the greatest credit on them and on the devoted staff of the school.

MERU

MERU A Potted History

**Medical Engineering
Research Unit
8 Damson Way, Orchard Hill,
Carshalton, Surrey SM5 4NR**
Registered Charity Number 269804

The Medical Engineering
Research Unit, now based at
Orchard Hill on what was once
Queen Mary's Hospital For
Children site at Carshalton,
Surrey, is probably unique in
both its organisation and in the
work it carries out. It is a combined effort of volunteers offering their
skills on a part time basis working with the Unit's technicians to meet
the specific needs of disabled children and young adults. This is all
done at no charge to the recipients.

The work of the Unit

The work of the unit utilises and explores the interface between
medicine and engineering in an endeavour to benefit disabled
children. Each project is undertaken for an individual child or young
adult with problems or requirements that cannot be satisfied by
commercially available equipment. Any type of equipment required
can be discussed, then designed and made in workshops by
appropriately skilled personnel. Referrals can be made by anyone
caring for a disabled child, preferably in liaison with a qualified
health worker.

Foundation of the Unit

The development and history of MERU is an interesting
example of how the ideas of one person can be translated into reality
and grow into a successful and valuable organisation.

In 1963, Mr WTF Bond, Senior Lecturer in Engineering Design

organised a club at the Borough Polytechnic (now South Bank University, London) to bring together people who were interested in the engineering problems of the whole field of medicine. Regular meetings were held but were hampered by lack of clinical stimulus and outlets.

In March 1970 the late Mr T. L. Bowen, Consultant Orthopaedic surgeon, attended one of these meetings to discuss the design of equipment for disabled children. The lack of clinical facilities soon became obvious and the members of the Club were invited to Queen Mary's Hospital For Children at Carshalton where a formal meeting was held between the members of the club and representatives of all the departments of the hospital. Meetings of the club continued at the Polytechnic but were now attended by members of the hospital staff. Monthly project meetings were held at the hospital to register and discuss new ideas and projects, allocate priorities and to control the Group's activities at Queen Mary's.

By adding spare time to some research time, Bill Bond was able to attend Queen Mary's for at least a whole day a week, thus coming into regular contact with both patients and staff. His contribution was recognised by the hospital Management Committee in the Autumn of 1970 when he was appointed Honorary Consulting medical Engineer.

Within a few months, medical engineering had become established as an invaluable adjunct to the care and management of disability, but without more time, personnel and facilities the many requirements around the hospital could not be satisfied. It was decided therefore to seek funds from charity sources in order to build a Department of Medical Engineering in the hospital grounds. Through the generosity of the National Fund for Research into Crippling Diseases, it became possible to employ a technician/ engineer and to purchase equipment and materials.

In 1972 a generous grant from the Triangle trust allowed the conversion of a building (B6) that the Hospital management Committee kindly made available. This building was formally opened by Lord Aberdare, Minister of State, Department of Health and Security on Saturday, 28th July 1973.

Continuing grants from the National Fund (Action Research) funded the employment of further technicians and the important help of the executive secretary. Business executives donated valuable time to administrative details and organised fund raising to assist the work of the Unit. This supplemented the help given by the Area health Authority. Additionally, Round Table Clubs and other community organisations sponsored special projects and other generous donors helped, especially Phillips Electronics at Mitcham, to equip very modern workshops and supported the design and manufacture of many projects. This resulted in an expanding field of liaison with medical staff to provide many forms of therapy from play to progressive development projects, aids to improve the living of patients, new types of equipment for surgery, new technologies and many ideas that help with the care and management of disablement.

By 1988 the unit had grown to such an extent, both in its salaried and volunteer staff and with the amount of machinery and equipment that had been donated, that its existing building proved too small and inadequate. The hospital authorities then provided a building (C6) that was no longer needed and the entire contents of B6 were removed and installed in its new home.

However, with the dramatic changes in the nature of health care in recent years, the emphasis had now been put on caring for disabilities out in the community. The Unit found that the disabled children it was catering for were no longer being admitted to the Hospital which was becoming increasingly concerned with children with acute needs.

The unit found that the severely disabled children it was set up to help and assist, with of course the important exception of those still resident at the Hospital who had grown up at Queen Mary's and knew no other home, were now living in the outside world. This meant that a radical change took place in the functioning of the Unit.

The children the Trust sought to help were now attending the special schools provided for them by the Local Education Authorities, with the input from the medical staff of Queen Mary's. They were now attending the special schools during term time and living in their family home with their parents and brothers and sisters when not at school.

MERU has responded to these dramatic changes and to the whole aspect of treating disabled children in the community by expanding its services into those communities.

In June 1993 the Unit once again moved to another building on the QMH site. This move came about because of the transfer of the Children's Hospital to St Helier. MERU then moved to 8, Damson Way on Orchard hill side of the QMH site that is now administered by the Merton and Sutton Community Health care Services.

The move was an opportunity for the Unit to adapt its new building to cater for a more modern and far-seeing approach to engineering and its uses in dealing with the problems of disabled children.

The Future of MERU

Recent experience has indicated to the Unit that although excellent craft skills that we have in abundance are still urgently needed to design and make the traditional equipment for disabled children, the ever growing need is in the world of communications and electronic devices. It is the intention of MERU that we will move with, and respond to, the new demands made upon us by the Carers who are working with disabled children and young adults and all MERU's future staff and volunteer recruitment will reflect this intention.

December 1994

The following article is reproduced by kind permission of the Croydon Advertiser Group:

KATHY MURPHY visits a special unit whose work is unique and invaluable ... yet it survives on voluntary contributions

The pleasure machines

It is often said that money can't buy happiness.

But like most well-known sayings, this is not strictly true.

There may well be some rich tycoons who are as miserable as sin.

But there are also plenty of impoverished people whose lives would run more smoothly aided by a little extra cash.

The can be said of most worthwhile voluntary projects.

While it is unusual for them to lack for enthusiasm and ideas, they are often prevented from realising their full potential because of lack of finance.

No one could argue that making the crippled lives of mentally and physically handicapped children more pleasant and fulfilling is well worthwhile.

Yet a group of people who are doing just that have to struggle for almost every penny they get.

The Trefor Bowen Medical Engineering Research Unit at Queen Mary's Hospital, Carshalton, gets no official financial support. It survives entirely on voluntary contributions.

Yet the work carried out by this unit, designing and producing equipment and aids for the sick and disabled, is unique and invaluable.

A teenage boy crippled by spina bifida, who whizzes round the hospital grounds in a specially-designed electric racing car, could not put a price on his joy. He is just glad that someone has finally discovered a way for him to get out and about without the wheelchair which so clearly labels him as disabled and different.

And what value can be put on the first attempts at speech coaxed from a mentally handicapped child by a cuddly panda stuffed with sensitive equipment so that its eyes light up when you shout at him?

Or how about the simple yet revolutionary aid which stops crutches from slippling on slippery floors?

Or an alarm that lets busy nurses know when a sick baby has wet its nappy?

All these and many more invaluable aids have been discovered and realised by the unit.

There is no argument about how much its work is needed.

Scores of human problems which can be met by mechanical solutions are fed constantly to the engineers at the unit by nurses, doctors, therapists, teachers and patients.

But sometimes, because of lack of time or finance, they have to remain just good ideas.

The story of the unit is really the story of two men, both experts in their own fields, who met by chance and discovered their mutual interest in helping others.

One was Mr Bill Bond, a consultant design engineer and lecturer in engineering design, and the other Mr Trefor Bowen, a leading orthopaedic surgeon.

At a design club in London founded by Mr Bond, Mr Bowen spoke of the problem of finding suitable equipment for disabled children.

It was a subject in which Mr Bond was deeply interested.

Together the two men set about turning a dream into reality – an engineering design unit actually within a hospital, and meeting the specific and individual needs of patients and staff.

Eventually their joint enthusiasm proved catching.

They managed to win the attention of a charitable organisation and individuals who provided enough money to establish the unit in a hut in the grounds of the hospital, with two full-time technicians.

Tragically Mr Bowen died last year at an early age from leukaemia. Today the unit bears his name as a permanent memorial to his work.

Mr Bond, now honorary consultant medical engineer for the hospital, spends one full day a week working at the unit as its director.

Every week there are new patients for him to help. Some present conditions which have baffled the medical world for decades; some have individual problems that may never recur.

How do you measure the angle of a baby's hip displacement?

How can you get a mentally handicapped child with a

wandering mind to concentrate his attention?

How does a wheelchair-bound child pick up a dropped ball?

How do you give a new-born baby oxygen during an operation?

Frequently the answers to such questions pop into Bill Bond's mind immediately. Sometimes they take weeks.

Then measurements have to be taken, solutions discussed, drawings made, prototype models constructed, tested, adapted and working models produced.

Because the unit's main work is for children, the resulting equipment often has the appearance of a toy. But the purpose is always much more than play.

Some exercises and therapy needed regularly by disabled children can become tedious and tiring and because staff have to be present to give constant encouragement, the demands on manpower are very great.

Bill Bond and his team have produced many machines which turn these tasks into a pleasure for the young patients at the hospital.

A child will often spend happy hours at a machine which rewards manual skill by paying out a sweet and setting off a musical roundabout, while repetitive exercises to strengthen crippled limbs can quickly become a chore.

But Mr Bond does not want to see his kind of work confined only to helping the young.

His vision is for medical engineering design units as part of every local community throughout the country and, eventually, throughout the world. Helping sick, disabled and mentally handicapped children and adults in and out of hospital.

The units, he is sure, would, like the one at Queen Mary's, quickly become a focal point for financial contributions and voluntary work from professional experts, local industries, colleges, universities, businessmen and many others enthusiastic to make some contribution.

"The great thing about a unit like ours is that the experts are constantly in touch with the people they are seeking to help," said Mr Bond.

"At Queen Mary's we have no red tape at all. If someone, anyone, has an idea or a problem, they just walk through the door of the unit and tell us about it.

"Useful comments are continually fed back to the unit from the wards. New ideas are constantly suggested by the medical staff who have now become design-minded.

"Also parents, patients and teachers can be considered part of the design team.

"Often, too, simply by just being on the spot the design engineer can see ways in which he can help.

"He can see how simply difficult things can be made easy.

"The other day I was walking though a ward when I saw a nurse propping up a baby with pillows. The child had a heart disease and had to lie at the right angle.

"I was able to suggest that we made an adjustable board so that she could do it just right."

But the fulfilment of Mr Bond's vision is severely hampered by lack of finance.

At the moment they find it difficult to keep up with the needs of Queen Mary's alone, although they know they could be of great help to other hospitals in the group.

Charities, the League of Friends, local Rotary Clubs and private and commercial donations keep them going from year to year.

But if the unit is to have a secure future and thrive and expand, official cash is essential.

As the consultant paediatric surgeon, Mr Herbert Eckstein, put it: "The major problem for the unit has been financial.

"I have felt that we have had to spend far too much time trying to find money, rather than spend our time thinking up new and better aids for the handicapped."

MERU (Medical Engineering Resource Unit)

Purpose:

To design and manufacture for individual disabled children, free of charge, aids, devices and equipment that are not available commercially.

To research and develop devices and equipment that have a more widespread use for defined disabled groups or conditions at no cost to the group or individuals. To provide a free advisory service for carers and parents relating to the availability, or not, of special equipment for their disabled child.

Main Activities:

The emphasis is on the design and engineering of "one off" pieces of equipment for children with disabilities of whom at least 60% have learning difficulties of various degrees. We are often looked on as the last resort when special equipment is urgently required. MERU operates through a mix of Volunteers and University Students offering their skills unpaid, working with the salaried MERU staff in our well-equipped workshops and electronics and computer departments.

Established:
28th July 1973

Address:
8 Damson Way, Orchard Hill,
Carshalton, Surrey, SM5 4NR

Telephone: 0208 770 8286
Facsimile: 0208 770 8398
Email: anyone@meru.co.uk
Web Site: www.meru.co.uk

Registered Charity No.:
269804

Founders:
W. F. Bond C.Eng., F.I.Mech.E.,
F.I.E.E., F.I.E.D. &
Mr Trefor Liwellyn-Bowen
F.R.C.S.

Chairman:
G. F. Sheppard B.Sc. (Hons),
C.Eng., M.I.Mech.E., F.I.M.I.

Manager:
John Welch BA (Hons.)

Total paid staff:
Full time: Five
Part time: Three

Total Volunteers:
Trustees: Five
Hands on volunteers: Twelve

Children we help:
Children with Physical Disabilities and Learning Difficulties including Cerebral Palsy, (spastic, ataxic, athetoid, paraplegic, hemeplegic, microcephalic), Duchenne Muscular Dystrophy, Spinal Muscular Dystrophy, Spinal Muscular Atrophy, Retts Syndrome, San Fillipo Mucopolysacanipe, Achondroplasia, Arthrogryposis, Spina Bifida/ Hydrocephalic, Osterogenesis Imperfecta (Brittle Bone), and disabled through birth trauma or injury, Head Injury through Road Traffic Accidents or other traumatic accidents.

Current Projects:
For the very latest projects please visit our web site or see our "Current Projects" brochure.

Two Major Projects that are in progress or are about to start:

The Elspeth Seating System is a method of automatically repositioning disabled children in their wheelchairs.

The Interface Centre is a centre where children come to be assessed for their ability to use computers where they are then supplied with accessing switches and devices designed and made by MERU. We have many other projects in progress or that have been recently completed which are too numerous to mention here but that we wish to share our results and findings at no cost' with any organisation helping disabled children.

Helpers of Queen Mary's Hospital for Children
(Medical Engineering Unit) Limited
is a registered Charity No. 269804 and
a Company Limited by Guarantee and
Not Having A Share Capital No. 1214125
Registered in England and Wales
and governed by Memorandum and Articles of Association.

MERU

Current Projects

Summer 2000

Switches and Controls

We have a complete range of special switches that have been designed for individual children. For every switch we make we make a second one to put into our MERU assessment kit. This enables us to try a whole range of switching devices with every child we see. If none of these meet the need we then go and make one that will. Any organisation that has problems with designing switches for the child in their care can approach us for advice and information and can borrow, for a short term, any switch in the kit that might provide a solution to the particular problem.

Fine & light touch controls (above) and heavier duty switches (below) for gross and ataxic movement.

Electronic Projects

We are continuously involved with projects requiring electronic input. These include remote control switches, wired switches, communication aids and devices, electronic objects of reference, special mice for computer work, and upgrades and alterations to computers to enable disabled children to access them. We are about to embark, together with other organisations, on a major project to make communication devices easier to access and more user friendly.

Surgical Equipment MERU will make, when required, special surgical equipment for surgeons operating on disabled children where there is no commercial alternative. We have designed and made Arthroscopy frames, spinal operating frames, leg supports and numerous varieties of specialist surgical instruments to each surgeon's special requirements.

Interface Centre

The Children's **Interface Centre** at our Unit looks at the needs of, and the problems met by, disabled children when accessing their computers. We, unlike other assessment centres, look at these needs in a holistic way. Whereas the obvious need is for the child to actually operate the computer by suitable accessing devices, equal attention is given to the child's seating position and the provision of trays and worktops and special attention is paid to the ergonomics of the child's workspace. MERU is endeavouring to provide for all these needs for each individual child who comes to our Centre for assessment.

Particular attention is paid to the problems met by children with disabilities, and their carers, who are attending main stream schools.

We offer free assessments to children who in the main part have severe physical disabilities and who might benefit from increased access to computers. We assist children in mainstream and special schools.

The field of service incorporates children living in North Surrey and South West London. Projects from children living further afield are occasionally considered, however we do ask that children and their carers make arrangements to visit us. If this is not possible we are happy to advise you of any local or national organisation that may be able to assist, and to provide information that will help. A catalogue of past projects can be seen on our Web site.

AirChair

Made at MERU to enable disabled children to travel on aeroplanes with upper body support and in comfort. More than 30 children have used the prototype chair (seen left) so far. Due to the demand for the chair we have found a manufacturer to make a batch of fifty that will be on sale to airlines who wish to offer this facility to their passengers.

For more information on the AirChair contact Jason Cole at Daws Engineering Ltd of Dorking 01306 881546.

Customised Trays

During the last 12 months we have been involved in a design project where the subject of customised trays for wheelchairs has been explored. From this project various tray designs have been tried with some findings indicate that mass production of a basic tray for all purposes does not work. Each child is an individual with their own special needs and trays must be designed for those particular needs.

Award for MERU Volunteer

Malcolm Reid, our volunteer cabinet maker, has been given an award by the Whitbread Volunteer Action Awards 2000 Committee.

Malcolm comes to our Unit 3 days a week bringing with him a life time of experience. With these skills he makes beautiful pieces of special furniture for disabled children, whilst passing on his knowledge and craft skills to our university students and high school students who come here for work experience.

Major Projects about to start

The Elspeth Project

This is an ambitious R&D project where the objective is to design a wheelchair seating position that can be adjusted electronically to suit the child's needs. The project will use existing automotive technology to solve many of the problems involved in achieving this. We have made the first working prototype and the early signs are that it will prove successful in the long run. We will progress further with this as we raise the funds needed to complete the project.

Major Projects just completed

Hoist slings for children with Disabilities

We have just finished a 12 month project investigating the problems involved when lifting and transferring disabled children from chair to chair, especially in main stream schools. The resultant report is available free of charge to all interested parties. Please contact Jan on 020 8770 8286.

Some Everyday MERU Projects

Light weight Chariot

This lightweight chariot was made for a little boy with Arthrogryposis to help him with his mobility, and to develop his skills if he eventually has to use a wheelchair, and to have fun with his friends.

Bespoke seating

MERU, drawing on 27 years experience, can cater for most special seating needs for individual children. Pictured right is a MERU corner chair specially designed and made for a baby girl with Achondroplasia. Because she is so tiny no market version was small enough to give her adequate support.

Stripey seating system

Patented by MERU, Stripey is a versatile system that allows a chair to be quickly made to suit an individual child's needs. It can be an in-car support (left), doubling up as an in-car seat, used in a swimming pool (see cover photo), a bath seat, a push chair insert and even a potty chair.

About MERU

Purpose: To design and manufacture for individual disabled children, free of charge, aids, devices and equipment that are not available commercially.

To research and develop devices and equipment that have a more widespread use for defined disabled groups or conditions at no cost to the group or individuals.

To provide a free advisory service for carers and parents relating to the availability, or not, of special equipment for their disabled child.

Main Activities: The emphasis is on the design and engineering of "one off" pieces of equipment for children with disabilities of whom at least 60% have learning difficulties of various degrees. We are often looked on as the last resort when special equipment is urgently required. MERU operates through a mix of Volunteers and University Students offering their skills unpaid, working with the salaried MERU staff in our well-equipped workshops and electronics and computer departments.

For more information about MERU and what we do and how we do it please see our Web Site www.meru.co.uk or ask for MERU's Information Brochure.

Medical Engineering Resource Unit

8 Damson Way, Orchard Hill
Carshalton, Surrey SM5 4NR

Tel.	020 8770 8284/6 Fax 020 8770 8398
	E-Mail; anyone@meru.co.uk
	Web site; www.meru.co.uk

Registered Charity No. 269804

SISTER MONEY

This chapter has been kindly contributed by Sister Joy Money.

My first ward as Sister

We had a pageant and the patients are dressed as wounded soldiers and me as Florence Nightingale. The lady in the corner with the child on the carriage is Mary Doyle.

Taken opposite D10 when it was made into Sick Bay which was previously on Hospital West 5-8 at the top of the main drive. The wooded area opposite D9 and D10 was known as the Bird Sanctuary. There were a large number of birds and the dawn chorus when you were on night duty was really beautiful.

This is Sister Beaman and Ward Orderly Hilda Dowie at Sick Bay.

This is Polly, the first of the horses I remember at the hospital which sadly died. 'Dan' looked after the horses and the grass.

247

'Daffa' - I acquired this photograph from Dan. He was devoted to the horses and slept with them when they were ill.

(Dan is remembered by Joe Smith in Book I)

The main drive looking up from A1/2. Getting around was very hard work.

Sunday morning service in the Chapel

Extract from THE POST IN SUTTON
Thursday May 18 1989

Peter Jones recalls the 80 year history of one of the country's top hospitals for children.

A LEGACY OF CARING

Eighty years ago, on January 29, 1909, the Children's Infirmary opened at Carshalton with accommodation for 900 patients.

Most of the children were from poor backgrounds and suffered from such conditions as surgical tuberculosis, rheumatic diseases and poliomyelitis.

Now called Queen Mary's Hospital for Children, the old Children's Infirmary is the largest children's hospital in the United Kingdom, offering a comprehensive service not only to local people but to patients from all over the country.

It was in 1911, the year of the coronation of King George V, that Queen Mary became the patron and the name of the hospital was changed.

In the years between the two world wars, the hospital's fame grew as a centre for the long term treatment of children.

Just 13 months after the outbreak of the second world war, in October 1940, the hospital was bombed for the first time, and during the rest of the war gained the dubious distinction of being the most frequently bombed hospital in the London area.

Mercifully, because of the scattered nature of the hospital, injuries were few and work continued as usual until June 1944 when the Government decided that, in view of the danger from V2 rockets, the patients would have to be evacuated. As a result the hospital was empty until after VJ Day.

The National Health Service was established in 1948 and Queen Mary's became a general children's hospital able to cater for all types of disorder ranging from major surgery of the newborn child to the care of the permanently disabled.

In June 1959, it was decided that the Fountain Hospital in Tooting should be closed and its child patients were transferred to Queen Mary's.

The work goes on. During 1988, 6500 in-patients and 13,500

accident and emergency cases plus 33,000 out-patients were seen and treated.

Queen Mary's is listed in the Guinness Book of Records as the largest children's hospital in the United Kingdom.

To celebrate its 80th anniversary, the people who run the hospital have laid on a series of events throughout the summer, which started with a dedication service in the Hospital Chapel on Monday.

On Thursday, May 25th, there will be an open day at the hospital's Rainbow Centre; then on May 27 a balloon race at the League of Friends Fete. On June 25, a charity celebrity cricket match and on July 12, a presentation to the students.

On September 9, there will be a children's fete then, finally, on December 9, a staff dinner dance.

MEMORIES

One of Queen Mary's earliest patients, 82 year old Mrs Elizabeth Mapston, returned to the hospital on Monday to take part in the commemorative service that began the 80th anniversary celebrations.

Born in the Lambeth Walk, she fell downstairs at the age of three and developed a tubercular spine. She was sent to Queen Mary's in 1912 and spent nine years in plaster. She was eventually discharged at the age of 15.

Mrs Mapston shook hands with Queen Mary when she officially opened the Hospital.

SERVICE TO COMMEMORATE THE 80th ANNIVERSARY
OF
QUEEN MARY'S HOSPITAL FOR CHILDREN

CONDUCTED BY: *The Hospital Chaplains*
PREACHER: *Frank Topping*
CHOIR: *Wallington High School for Boys*

251

ORDER OF SERVICE

HYMN: "Now thank we all our God" (Tune: Nun Danket)

1. Now thank we all our God,
   With heart and hand and voices,
   Who wondrous things hath done,
   In whom his world rejoices;
   Who from his mother's arms
   Hath blessed us on our way
   With countless gifts of love,
   And still is ours today.

2. O may this bounteous God
   Through all our life be near us,
   With ever joyful hearts
   And blessed peace to cheer us,
   And keep us in his grace,
   And guide us when perplexed,
   And free us from all ills
   In this world and the next.

3. All praise and thanks to God
   The Father now be given
   The Son, and him who reigns
   With them in highest heaven,
   The one eternal God,
   Whom earth and heaven adore,
   For thus it was, is now,
   And shall be evermore.

PRAYERS OF THANKSGIVING: Led by Rev. G. Lister

1st READING: LEVITICUS 19. 9-18
            Read by: Mr. G. L. Elderfield — General Manager

THE REVEREND FRANK TOPPING

Frank Topping was born into a Catholic family on Merseyside, and after drama training and National Service became stage manager/electrician and assistant carpenter with the Leatherhead Rep.

Continuing his career in theatre and television, Frank came under the influence of Derrick Greeves, the Minister of the Methodist Central Hall Westminster and regained his faith, eventually being ordained as a Methodist Minister in 1970.

His ministry started in a conventional way in Brighton but soon his skills as a communicator came to the fore, and he became Assistant Religious Broadcasting Organiser for BBC North, and later a network editor and contributor for many programmes.

Many know him for his writings and his broadcasting, while others associate him with the West End Show "Swann with Topping" in which he starred with Donald Swann.

He is now the chaplain to Kent College, Pembury.

HYMN: "Help us to help each other Lord"

1. Help us to help each other Lord,
Each other's cross to bear,
Let each his friendly aid afford,
And feel his brother's care.

2. Help us to build each other up,
Our little stock improve;
Increase our faith, confirm our hope,
And perfect us in love.

3. Up into Thee, our living head,
Let us in all things grow,
Till Thou hast made us free indeed,
And spotless here below.

4. Then, when the mighty work is wrought,
Receive Thy ready bride;
Give us in heaven a happy lot,
With all the sanctified. Amen.

2nd READING: Luke 10 25-37
Read by Rev. Howard Smith

ANTHEM: Choir

ADDRESS: By the Reverend Frank Topping

PRAYERS OF INTERCESSION:
Led by Fr. K. Pelham

Our Father who art in heaven,
Hallowed be Thy name;
Thy Kingdom come, Thy will be done
On earth as it is in heaven.
Give us this day our daily bread,
And forgive us our trespasses,
As we forgive those who trespass against us,
And lead us not into temptation
But deliver us from evil,
For thine is the Kingdom,
The power, and the glory,
For ever and ever. Amen.

HYMN: "Praise my soul the King of heaven"

1. Praise my soul the King of heaven,
To his feet thy tribute bring;
Ransomed, healed, restored, forgiven,
Who like me his praise should sing?
Alleluia! Alleluia!
Praise the everlasting King.

2. Praise him for his grace and favour
To our fathers in distress;
Praise him still the same as ever,
Slow to chide, and swift to bless:
Alleluia! Alleluia!
Glorious in his faithfulness.

3. Father-like, he tends and spares us,
Well our feeble frame he knows;
In his hands he gently bears us
Rescues us from all our foes;
Alleluia! Alleluia!
Widely as his mercy flows.

4. Angels, help us to adore him;
Ye behold him face to face;
Sun and moon, bow down before him,
Dwellers all in time and space:
Alleluia! Alleluia!
Praise with us the God of Grace.

BLESSING

RECEPTION: To be held in Post-Graduate Medical Centre

THE RAINBOW CENTRE

The Rainbow Centre was opened in 1982 by Princess Alexandra. It cost £98,000 and was greatly aided by public fund raising. HUTCH (Help Us Treat Child Handicap) raised £48,000 alone.

Its function was as an out-patient unit where children with developmental problems could be seen with their families by a professional team in an informal setting. The building had a reception area, clinical room, a large playroom, a meeting room and offices.

Through a team of health professionals headed by a Consultant Paediatrician which included a Clinical Nursing Sister, Community Doctor, a Medical Social Worker, Psychologist Physiotherapist and Medical Secretaries co-ordinating all the work of the Centre, the children, parents and families were helped with coping and managing problems that arise from delayed development.

Opening of The Rainbow Centre
April 1982
by Princess Alexandra

PRINCESS RAINBOW

PRINCESS RAINBOW

A ray of hope shone through the grey skies when Princess Alexandra opened the Rainbow Centre at Queen Mary's Hospital for Children.

The Princess arrived to cheering, flag waving crowds, and accompanied by her Lady-in-Waiting unveiled the commemorative plaque before embarking on a tour of the grounds.

A number of the committee members of Help Us Treat a Handicapped Child who helped to get the project off the ground, were presented to her.

HUTCH raised nearly half the total cost of the assessment centre, and it was a big moment for Dr Josephine Hammond, consultant paediatrician and chairman of the charity, when she was presented to the Princess.

Dr Hammond wrote to Princess Alexandra to thank her for a donation and invited her to open the Rainbow Centre.

April 22, 1982

Sutton Borough News
April 22, 1982

THERE was a camera at the ready here when the Princess stopped for a chat.

Smiles all round the Rainbow

Sutton Borough News
April 22, 1982

Smiles all round the Rainbow

Princess Alexandra's visit to Queen Mary's Hospital for Children last week brought a smile to even the saddest faces.

Arriving in a black limousine, she officially opened the new Rainbow Centre, designed to help handicapped children although not before receiving a bouquet from six-year-old Jean-Paul Hegbourne.

The worried-looking lad handled the presentation like a professional and spoke a few words before the Princess moved on.

The centre, built at a cost of £98,000, was paid for by HUTCH, the Help Us Treat Child Handicap organisation, and the former Merton, Sutton and Wandsworth Area Health Authority. It is designed to detect child handicap and prevent delays in treatment.

In a speech to the nurses, doctors and administrators, Princess Alexandra said: "It is a great pleasure for me to return to Queen Mary's, the hospital which has one single aim, of bringing health and normality to all children whatever their illness." The last visit she paid to the hospital was to present prizes to nurses in 1969.

The Princess, on a guided tour of the grounds, decided to have a closer look at the hospital radio station. Radio Lollipop, staffed by enthusiastic young volunteers brings music and fun into the daily lives of Queen Mary's patients. The royal visitor was shown around by Lollipop's Headley Finn and Peter Bourke.

During the visit, Princess Alexandra met as many children as she could. She left them all with smiling faces, especially ten-year-olds Louise Desmond and Carla O'Brien who managed to take her picture.

"She is really pretty," said Carla, "and she has a lovely voice.

The tour ended with a reception for 150 guests held in the staff hall.

The Rainbow Centre

In the 1980s the government of the time allocated funds for 'assessment centres' for children with special needs. The funds for Queen Mary's Hospital for Children were used to extend the out-patients so new funds had to be raised when the Rainbow Centre was considered. The fundraising group HUTCH (Help Us Treat Child Handicap) raised £48,000 with enormous local support, especially from schools, and a large grant from the King Edward Fund. The (then) Area Health Authority met the remaining costs to a total of £98,000.

The Centre was opened in 1982 by Princess Alexandra. Later visitors included the Queen of Tonga.

The Centre's function was as an out-patient unit where children with developmental problems could be seen with their families by a professional team in an informal setting. The building included a reception centre, clinical rooms, a large playroom, a meeting room and offices.

Through a team of health professionals which included hospital and community paediatricians, a clinical nursing sister, a medical social worker, and psychologist, therapists and medical secretaries, and also input from educational psychology, co-ordinating the work of the centre, children were helped with coping and managing problems that arise with delayed development.

Sadly when QMHC moved to St Helier's Hospital in 1994, the Health Authority decided not to re-provide an identified unit for children with special needs.

Dr Josephine Hammond, Consultant Paediatrician

Flag waving, cheering crowds ensure
Welcome Fit for a Queen

A Royal smile

A lone woman knelt and prayed in the chapel of Queen Mary's Hospital for Children, Carshalton.

After the flag waving, noise and cheer of her visit, the Queen of Tonga stopped for a few minutes in the quiet of the chapel before lunching with staff and health authority officials.

Queen Halaevalu Mata'aho arrived at Queen Mary's last Friday with two attendants to be greeted by local children waving flags.

After a 30 minute chat about the work of the hospital, the Queen visited the Rainbow Centre, used for the early detection of children's handicaps.

The sun shone brightly as members of the Boys' Brigade formed a guard of honour and the hospital's radio station, Radio Lollipop, played The Blue Danube.

Her Majesty then toured wards where severely mentally and physically handicapped children are treated.

Queen Halaevalu Mata'aho had asked to see a hospital for handicapped children during her state visit with her husband to this country.

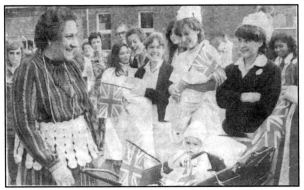

Queen Halaevalu Mata'aho talks to a group of nurses

"I was impressed with her knowledge of handicap problems," said Dr Ian Pickering, consultant.

The smiling Queen, wearing a dark silk dress with a pearl necklace and earrings and the ceremonial kie kie round her waist, was obviously touched by the youngest patients.

The visit to Queen Mary's marked the end of the King and Queen of Tonga's state visit, but they are staying unofficially with their daughter, who is expecting a third child, until the middle of November.

The News, November 3, 1983

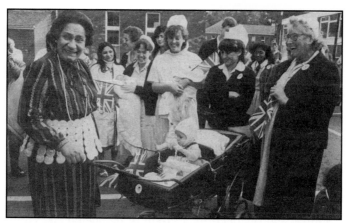

The Queen of Tonga made time for a leisurely tour of Queen Mary's Hospital for Children, Carshalton, Surrey, during her recent four day visit to the UK. As she chatted to staff and patients, the queen wore a ceremonial straw kie-kie - the Tongan equivalent, the Foreign and Commonwealth office tells us, of a hat and gloves. (NURSING MIRROR)

THE MINIATURE RAILWAY

"Much law, but little justice."

THE FOUNTAIN & CARSHALTON GROUP H.M.C.

OPENING OF MINIATURE RAILWAY

AT

QUEEN MARY'S HOSPITAL FOR CHILDREN,
CARSHALTON, SURREY.

ON

SATURDAY, 10TH MAY, 1969

Surveying & Building started May 27- d 1968.

ORDER OF PROCEEDINGS

11.30 a.m. Introduction:-
THE LORD GRENFELL, T.D.,
Chairman: Fountain and Carshalton Group
Hospital Management Committee.

- - - - - - - - - - -

Opening of the railway by THE WORSHIPFUL THE
MAYOR OF THE LONDON BOROUGH OF SUTTON,
ALDERMAN F.C. FINCH, J.P.

12.15 p.m. Buffet Luncheon in Coffee Room of the
Staff Residence.

This miniature railway has been installed
in the hospital thanks to the enthusiasm and
extremely hard work of Mr. J. Fowles, assisted
by the League of Friends and Hospital Management
Committee.
From the very high standard of maintenance
it will be obvious to all that Mr. Fowles is
a great railway enthusiast, but also by
allowing the hospital to be the site of his
railway, he will provide many hours of enjoyment
for the children of this hospital, and Parents
and Hospital Management Committee are indebted
to him for his kind action.

The Miniature Railway at Queen Mary's ran for a period of 29 years. Staffed and operated by a group of dedicated and enthusiastic volunteers it provided immense fun and pleasure to the children of Queen Mary's, as well as to parents, relations, staff, carers, friends and visitors.

Brian Jones' article that follows gives an interesting insight into the conception and development of the railway by Mr John Fowles, its founder, and its continuation by the Surrey Downs Railway Group.

Published here also are the notes of a meeting held on the 11th October 1971; photographs illustrating the railway carrying passengers around the vast and beautiful grounds of Queen Mary's Hospital and at the end of the chapter the very sad closure notice. Such a pity it was deemed necessary to close and withdraw such a wonderful service from the Orchard Hill residents.

22 May 1986

Not many people realise that Queen Mary's Hospital for Children, Carshalton, has its very own passenger carrying miniature railway and will probably be even more surprised to learn that this year is its eighteenth birthday.

The line which is ten and a quarter inch gauge, and approximately half a mile long, was started by a local enthusiast, Mr John Fowles, in 1968. He was looking for a suitable site, in the Borough of Sutton, to lay down some track in order to run the steam locomotives he owned and approached the hospital. They agreed on condition that he gave rides free to the children staying in the hospital and their visiting relatives, and this is the basis on which the railway still operates today.

Since 1968, however, a lot of changes have taken place. In 1971 John Fowles decided to retire, and move to Hampshire which unfortunately meant the loss of the steam locomotives, but the rest of the railway track, a couple of carriages, and a then new 'diesel' loco "SYD TYNDALL", were purchased for the hospital by the League of Friends. The remaining enthusiasts agreed to continue running the line for the hospital during the summer, in return for using the railway to build and run their own trains. The enthusiasts, now known as the Surrey Downs Railway Group, have since 1971, built the railway a low loader wagon to carry children in wheelchairs, extended the line in 1974 to its present length, and during the last six months have added a new terminus station near to the hospital school. During the last winter, the loco SYD TYNDALL was given a complete mechanical overhaul, making it an almost as new locomotive.

The railway has two other locomotives, "QUEEN SCOUT" - an accurate model of a British Rail 'Hymek' class locomotive which was bought for the hospital in 1982 by local Scout Groups, and a model of "TOBY THE TRAM ENGINE", built by a group member in 1983.

The railway runs every Sunday afternoon starting at 2.30 pm from May to September and welcomes all visitors, with the proviso that hospital children have priority. We currently have several projects to complete, including a new carriage shed (for some new carriages we desperately want!) and a signal box, but time and money are our main obstacles. We would be grateful to receive any donations to these whatever the amount. We would also be very interested in any local buisnesses which would be prepared to sponsor us, especially if they are connected with engineering.

Brian Jones

MINIATURE RAILWAY

NOTES OF MEETING HELD ON 11.10.71

Present: Messrs. Kennedy (Chairman)
Plumpton
Shrimpton
Smith
Mrs. Quack

Apologies for absence were received from Mr Crossley.

Mr Kennedy invited Mr Plumpton to report on the running of the railway from the drivers' point of view. Mr Plumpton said there had only been a few technical difficulties which had now nearly all been dealt with satisfactorily. Work has started on the building of a carriage which will enable four wheelchairs to be carried on the railway. Mr Shrimpton felt the League of Friends might well be willing to help with the expense incurred in building this carriage but Mr Plumpton said that he and his colleagues would very much like to provide this at their own expense as their gift to the children.

The railway had attracted the attention of various weekend visitors to the hospital who had been shown round the engine shed etc. Several of these people had expressed their special interest in railway by donations, totalling £2.50, and this sum has been sufficient to cover the cost of the oil used.

Mr Shrimpton asked whether there would be any costs incurred during the maintenance period in the winter. Mr Plumpton said there would only be one item of outlay - the initial hiring of oxygen and acetyline bottles at approximately £40 and subsequent refills at approximately £3. It was felt that help might be given for this either by the League of Friends or the hospital and Mr Shrimpton and Mrs Quack said they would look into this.*

Mr Plumpton reported that manually operated flashing lights had been installed at the level crossing by Ward C8 and it was planned to alter these in due course to automatic operation.

Mr Plumpton wondered whether a redundant hospital electric van and trailer could be made available for specified helpers to tour the wards to fetch the children to the railway on the occasions when there were not many helpers. Mrs Quack said she would make enquiries.**

---

*   The League of Friends are writing to tell Mr Plumpton that they will be pleased to pay the necessary £40, subject to the equipment used by Mr Plumpton meeting the recent new BOC regulations.

**   On enquiry it appears most unlikely that there will be any electric coach available for this purpose during the next twelve months.

Driver Brian Jones with Stuart

Brian Withers driving a very happy group of children. Justin Bradley is seated at the rear of the engine, which is a replica of the diesel engine, class 47 Hymek - QUEEN SCOUT

Justin driving his 'passengers' through the beautiful grounds of Queen Mary's Hospital for Children

Clive driving with Justin as the Guard

Brian driving a happy band of children past the ward playground

The next set of photographs were taken on 25th May 1996 at the last fete to be held on the original Queen Mary's site.

Richard driving TITAN

Dave driving SYD with Barry standing in the background

Barry driving QUEEN SCOUT

Richard driving TITAN

In the background is Brian Withers with Richard at the controls

David driving TITAN

Brian Withers - the controller

*London North Eastern Tram, known to the children as TOBY from
'Thomas the Tank Engine'*

QUEEN SCOUT being driven by Neal Catterall. Queen Scout was purchased in 1982 using funds raised by Sutton and Cheam Scouts. The locomotive was built by Mardyke Miniature Railways Ltd.

This engine was battery powered. It was nicknamed 'TOBY'. In the roof of the shed you can see a steel lintel; this with the hoist on the right was used for heavy maintenance. TOBY was built by Brian Jones at Queen Mary's Railway in the early 1980s. The engineer's name is Darren.

Queen Mary's Railway
Permanent Withdrawal of Passenger Services

The NHS Estates Executive have given notice for the removal of railway services between Queen Mary's Central and Orchard Hill Station from Monday 26 May 1997.

Railway passenger services will continue to run on the following dates ;
Sunday 04 May 1997 14.30 - 16.30
Sunday 11 May 1997 14.30 - 16.30
Sunday 18 May 1997 14.30 - 16.30
Saturday 24 May 1997 14.00 - 15.30
Sunday 25 May 1997 14.30 - 16.30

24 May is the League of Friends Fete.

If you require further information regarding closure of the railway, please write to :

Paul Dickinson
St Ann's House
St Ann's Road
Chertsey
Surrey

David Munton
NHS Estates
40 Eastbourne
Terrace
London W2 3QR

Headline from the Sutton Guardian, May 1997

EXTRACTS FROM LEAGUE OF FRIENDS NEWSLETTERS

Some years ago, the Friends of Queen Mary's Hospital for Children, Carshalton, decided that perhaps the greatest need for the long-stay mentally handicapped children in the hospital was to have a Holiday Home. They had, in fact, always gone to Osborne House at Hastings which is under the same administration but, notwithstanding, the League felt that their own Home would be something completely different and provide extra holidays etc.

An appeal was launched in order to build this Home. The sum - £40,000. Their first thought was to have a Home by the sea with a living-in caretaker, but at this time the prices of property rocketed and the chances of getting a settled living-in reliable help seemed somewhat unlikely. Winter care too would present a problem.

As the time approached when the appeal reached £20,000, the League went down to Selsey to look at a site where hundreds of mobile homes are situated and came away very impressed by the facilities provided, the standard of care and interest shown by the management and, consequently, other ideas began to form. After a lot of thought, an approach was made to the builder of the mobile homes. He was told of some of the practical difficulties experienced by severely handicapped children. Again, the League was impressed by the interest shown, together with the desire to please. The owner of the organisation, being himself handicapped, was appreciative of the League's needs.

The League's Holiday Home sub-committee then co-ordinated the builders of the mobile homes and the Selsey Holiday Centre and after three years the appeal was completed with sufficient money to provide three mobile homes. At the end of last summer, the League was able to send some children down to Selsey as two of the homes were on site and complete. Enormous co-operation was forthcoming from the hospital staff, so much so that they are looking forward to this year and plans are in operation to have the three homes in constant use until October.

The great bonus to the League has been the wonderful response which has been forthcoming from the children who have slotted well into the intimate family life in the mobile home and they say that they have heard some lovely stories of the children's reactions to living in the family environment.

Transport is a need and because of the very size of the site, the League will be providing a mini-bus. This will add to the enjoyment of the holiday, the opportunity to visit places of interest, easier access to the sea, and trips when the weather is not so kind.

That project over, the League is now turning its attention to the Hospital Zoo! £2,000 is being provided for its upgrading. £10,000 is also being provided for parents' accommodation on the very young children's paediatric ward, so that mothers can stay with very sick children in a homely atmosphere. The close proximity of a parent assisting so greatly in the recovery of a very sick infant. The League has also agreed to spend £15,000 on the mentally handicapped wards for the provision of furniture and equipment for a rumpus room. Much of this money is raised by the Friends in the shop and canteen which are run all the year round.

Letter to local press – December 1987

Dear Sir,

We, the Friends of Queen Mary's Hospital for Children, are only too aware that there is still considerable public concern about the future of Queen Mary's Hospital. We are therefore putting on record our understanding of the position as it is today.

It will be recalled that the future of Queen Mary's Hospital was bound up with the Merton and Sutton District Health Authority's Acute Services Strategy. The Authority's preferred solution was to rebuild Queen Mary's on a site adjacent to St Helier Hospital. We understand that this proposed strategy has been endorsed by the S.W. Thames Regional Health Authority and that detailed planning is now going forward for the building of a new, custom built children's hospital on the side adjacent to St Helier. This new hospital should be operational in early 1994.

The Friends have always considered that the best solution was to build a new hospital on the present Carshalton site, which we felt was, with its open air environment, ideal for such a hospital and we have made representations to the Authorities advocating this view. We feel, however, that the paramount consideration is that there should be a newly built and specially designed children's hospital. In these circumstances we feel that we should not run the risk of delaying, or prejudicing, such an outcome by further protest, since we feel that it best serves the interest of the children using the Hospital. It is nevertheless our intention to closely monitor developments to ensure that a new hospital is in fact built.

It should be emphasised that the facilities for the mentally handicapped residents, at present in Orchard Hill, a part of the Queen Mary's complex at Carshalton, will continue to be used for those residents.

The work of the Friends in its present form will still be needed over the next seven or so years, whilst the Hospital continues to exist at Carshalton and support from the public will still be sought.

Yours faithfully

Mrs P Heming
(Chairman)

Extract from League of Friends Newsletter – December 1987

The Hospital is extremely grateful for all the help and support given by the Friends in the past. We are now looking forward to a new era and hope to develop and improve our services in the coming years. We shall need the full support of an active League of Friends in order to achieve our aims, and hope that the Friends of Queen Mary's and Orchard Hill will continue their magnificent efforts in both fundraising and acting as ambassadors to promote the Hospital.

Philip Hurst
Operational Manager

Recent Expenditures

We have been somewhat worried that recent publicity surrounding the decision to rebuild the Queen Mary's part of the hospital on a different location would make our own fundraising more difficult. Certainly we would ask you all to make special efforts to ensure that money keeps coming in. Remember any real change is still at least seven years or more away and all the services and contributions we make must continue. Orchard Hill, so intimately connected with Queen Mary's continues in any case on the present site and our efforts are equally devoted to this section of the hospital.

Since our last newsletter we have:

Allocated £900 towards decorations and gifts for the wards at Christmas;

Had a demonstration of the 'gastroscope' which is now in use and to which we contributed £9,000;

Agreed to meet the cost of supplying armchairs and refurbishing the parent's relaxation room on Ward B8.

Newsletter – October 1994

From the Chair

It gives me great pleasure to be able to report that we have moved The Friends Centre from the QM site to St Heliers.

Once the move was completed Ruth Taylor began to organise things. It needed cleaning inside and out, repainting, some re-wiring and of course re-stocking. A new volunteer list needed to be put together. Ruth was very much instrumental in getting a team of volunteers together.

On September the 1st we had an official opening attended by the Mayor of Sutton and others from St Heliers and Queen Mary's.

On the 5th September, Ruth opened the doors for business. The Centre has been welcomed by parents and staff of Queen Mary's.

We do have a parking spot outside the Centre and hope to increase the car parking spaces to 3 in the near future.

A PICTORIAL HISTORY

The following collection of photographs are shown to illustrate the variety of activities enjoyed by children and staff, both at the hospital and elsewhere.

A number of the illustrations are shown with dates, though the majority have no specific date.

I have attempted to put them in some semblance of chronological order; however, a number may well be out of sequence.

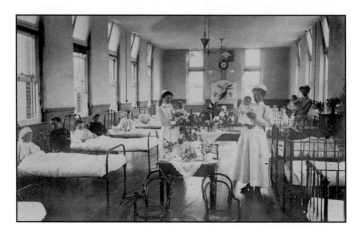

Wards B1 (above) and B2 (below) in 1910

The bearded gentleman in these photos is believed to be the first Superintendent doctor, Dr W T Gordon Pugh

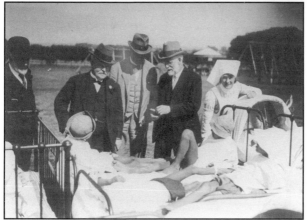

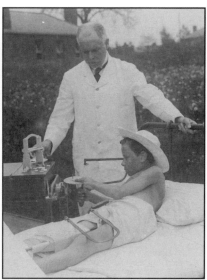

Queen Mary's from the air - 1925

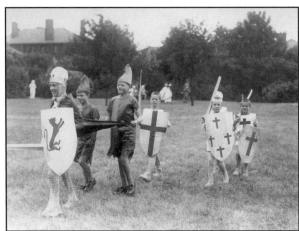

Pageant
July 1925

282

Having fun!

Ward Block B3 & B4 The last ward open - closed 30th November 1993 11.30 am

Ward B6 before it was bombed. It was later used as a workshop by the Medical Engineering Research Unit.

Hospital East

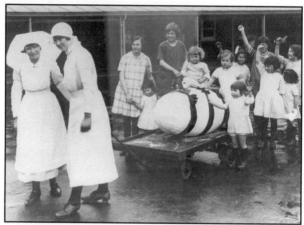

*Wintry scenes at
Queen Mary's*

*(photographs kindly
contributed by
Lesley Megan)*

Matron and Assistant Nurses - 1931

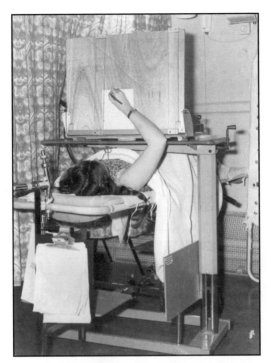

School Lesson

Fete 1954 - Head of "Ladybird", consternation of patient!

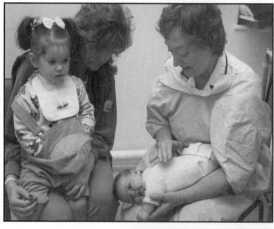

Mary and Grace at the Queen Mary's switchboard

Stenia Sawicka (left)
Louie Rudd-Clarke (right)
Nursing set 1965-68
Where is Stenia - does anyone
know?

Nurse Pauline Richmond
with Stuart Oliver

(all photos on this page
courtesy of Pauline Richmond)

Nurses Prizegiving 1968

MY OWN MEMORIES

My first experience of the problems faced by disabled people came at a very early age. During the war, along with my mother and brother, I was evacuated to Holmfirth, Yorkshire. Bombing raids having reached saturation level, and bombs falling close to our home in Tooting, South London, we said farewell to my father, who was engaged in vital war work, and left for Yorkshire. The evacuee trains were packed.

At Holmfirth, we were billeted in a large Manor House. It was there that we met Terry, his mother and brother, who had left their home in Eastbourne, Sussex, to escape to a safer environment. Terry had difficulty in walking and we were to learn later that he suffered from muscular dystrophy.

Returning to London when the situation became less dangerous, my mother kept in touch with the family. Eventually Terry could walk no longer and went to live at the Searchlight Home in Newhaven, Sussex. I used to visit Terry several times a year and made friends with his fellow sufferers John and Steve. A more courageous trio you could not wish to meet. Sadly, Terry, Steve and John passed away.

During my teacher training, I had thoughts of one day working with those who, like my friends, had been born, or become, disabled in any way. On 8th May 1972, I became a teacher at Queen Mary's Hospital for Children and stayed there until its transfer to St Helier's on 30th November 1993.

Owing to the closure of my previous school and wanting to work at the wonderful Queen Mary's Hospital, I took on as a temporary post that of a porter until a vacancy occurred in one of the hospital schools. Life as a porter was interesting and varied. I made many friends during this period and some of the friendships have lasted until the present day.

Mr Jim Palmer was Head Porter and he offered to promote me to the position of Hall Porter. While I was considering this my application for a teaching post in the Fountain School was approved

I have many happy memories of my days as a porter and like all other employment in the hospital the end result was to help sick and handicapped children. There was great camaraderie between the porters and they made me very welcome.

Teaching children with severe learning disabilities was a new experience for me and the Act of Parliament bringing these children under the control of the Department for Education had only come into force on the lst April 1971. Soon realising that there was a great deal to be learnt concerning the education of these children, I carried out a study and wrote a paper on the subject which is published in this book.

Working mainly on the wards I also witnessed the outstanding work of the medical and paramedical staff. Their co-operation and support I valued.

There were many happy but sometimes very sad times. One of my happiest memories was that of flying a kite with a young lad who was seriously ill. I arrived on the ward one winter's morning to find him in the courtyard at the rear of the ward, with a nurse, trying to fly a kite. However, they were not having much success. Seeing this going on I offered to assist them. (When I was a young boy my father had made kites for me and taught me how to fly them).

On the ward that morning were several children of school age. I asked the staff if they would supervise their school work while I went out with this lad and showed him how to fly a kite. We spent the rest of the morning out on the field behind B2, running up and down, flying the kite above the ward roofs. Eventually, it got stuck in a tree and, despite our valiant efforts, we could not free it.

Returning to the ward, we cleaned as much mud from ourselves as we could, having had great fun. Sadly the child died within the year. I am always thankful to this day that we had that most exhilarating and enjoyable time together, made possible by the co-operation of the ward staff.

Over a twenty-two year period many events and stories unfolded: being Father Christmas at the Fountain School parties and getting jelly and ice-cream squashed into my beard; listening to the children's jokes; my discussions with parents; the prayers at the bedside from the Chaplain and his team; a boy arriving on a stretcher straight from surgery and asking if he could have some schoolwork; the courage co-operation and willingness of the children to study; helping parents to cope with a sudden crisis; and words and letters of thanks which were always appreciated.

Every day on the wards brought new experiences and new challenges. They were met and tackled wherever possible. It was a privilege to be there.

CONCLUSION

Illness, disease and disability have been prevalent since life began. Treating and curing diseases has occupied and baffled the minds of people through the centuries. Some like Jenner, who found the answer to smallpox by observation rather than scientific experiment, have prevented much suffering and death. Doctors, nurses and scientists have by their research, compassion and dedication, relieved the suffering of millions throughout the world.

This century has witnessed a cultural, economic, social, political and scientific revolution. Gone are the days when healthcare was primarily dependent on wealth. Even before the days of the National Health Service some doctors and nurses gave their services free to the poor or charged very little for their treatment. I remember my parents paying our doctor two shillings and sixpence a visit when my brother, sister and myself caught Scarlet Fever, in that order, soon after the end of the Second World War.

Every generation has had its own peculiar problems. Outbreaks of various diseases have occurred throughout the ages and on each occasion have been combated wherever possible.

For most of the 20th Century, Queen Mary's Hospital for Children played a key role in the treatment and cure of disease and disability. From the work of people like Dr. Pugh and Sister Elizabeth Kenny, to the present day ministrants to the sick.

Many children owe the quality of life they now enjoy to the treatment that they received at Queen Mary's. A hospital that has been a flagship for all that is good and noble of treatment.

From the preceding pages and photographs can be read and seen the way in which the hospital came to be respected world-wide for its standard of excellence in childcare treatment.

The 136 acre site on which it once stood gave opportunity originally for fresh air and sunshine treatment to London children living in damp, squalid and impoverished conditions which I have witnessed first hand. As the years progressed so it extended its treatment on a national and international basis.

During its time, Queen Mary's has undergone many changes and moved to the new site at the St Helier NHS Trust Hospital on the 30th November 1993.

Many reasons for these changes can be given. Among them, two world wars. After the evacuation during the second world war and its resumption again at Carshalton, the number of beds were reduced by approximately one third of the original total.

Government legislation in 1959 changed it to a comprehensive children's hospital, the first of its kind in the country.

Social, political and cultural changes have had their impact on Queen Mary's as they have done everywhere else in society. How community care is now prevalent in treatment of disease after the acute stage of illness is over. Long stay hospitals have become a feature of the past.

The work of many professionals in healthcare and education has altered dramatically. Hospital school teachers are now not such a common feature of children's wards. Children's length of stay is now rather a case of days and weeks rather than years.

With its spacious and beautiful grounds, Queen Mary's was a unique landmark on its original site, one that we are unlikely to witness again. In this book, I have tried to capture the spirit of the hospital.

All those associated with Queen Mary's played a vital role in the work of healing. Whether it was the kind and dedicated work of the staff, the loving parents, or those who provided the funds, or others through their voluntary work – like the League of Friends Volunteers. A common purpose and bond prevailed throughout.

May all those who work with the sick be blessed with the gift of healing hands and loving hearts.